LIVING BEHIND THE
MASK

Ella Havell

LIVING BEHIND THE MASK

First Published 2006

PUBLISHED BY:
SMILE Creative Promotions Ltd
1 Lexden Mews
Lexden Road
Colchester
Essex   CO3 4DA
Tel: 01206 577902
E-Mail EllaHavell@aol.com
www.smilepuppetministry.org.uk
ISBN: 978-0-9552214-0-8

© Ella Havell 1999: Living Behind The Mask

DESIGN & PRODUCTION
Footsteps Design & Marketing
01206 272 967
studio@footsteps-design.co.uk

ACKNOWLEDGEMENTS

I want to dedicate this book to the Lord. Without Him, my life would not be worth living.

I want to thank everyone involved at this time for being there for me, especially my good friends - Colette, Linda, Terry & Linda, Jennifer, Debbie, Teresa , Ajay & Rosanna and everyone else who was involved with this prayer month. You are all very special to me.

I would also like to give a big thank you to Bet and Roy for baby-sitting for us and supporting us through the years. You made a difficult time more manageable, it is sad Betty is not here with us any longer, she is deeply missed but is now with the Lord.

Also I would like to say a thank you to Helena Wilkinson for the support and wisdom she has given me over the years, Jennifer Rees Larcombe for the inspiration and comfort she was and is.

I want to say to Mum, Dad and Shane that I love you and I am sorry for the pain I have caused you over the years.

For the continued support, love and grace from friends and family at Kingsland Church, especially Dave & Sarah, Neil & Maggie, Jenny, Paul and Simon , the gap year changed my life even further.

Two more people for being there for me, my best friend Paula, who has stuck with me through thick and thin for being a true friend, love you. .And, of course, a big thank you to my darling husband John, thank you for your encouragement. I love you.

God Bless and thank you.

Love Ella
X X X

Living Behind the Mask

This is a story of love, of God's unconditional love expressed through a community of faithful Christians. It tells of one woman's journey from isolation and desolation to joy and transformation through a lovingly structured programme of support and commitment.

This account of Christianity in action provides a powerful example of how the words of Christ can transform lives in today's world.

> *"The desert and the parched land will be glad; the wilderness will rejoice and blossom. Like the crocus, it will burst into bloom; it will rejoice greatly and shout for joy ..."*
>
> *"Be strong, do not fear; your God will come...*
> *He will come to save you".*
> *Isaiah 35*
>
> *"Humble yourselves, then, under God's mighty hand, so that he will lift you up in his own good time. Leave all your worries with him, because he cares for you."*
> *1 Peter 5: 6-7.*

PREFACE

There are many different perceptions of what an eating disorder is. Some think it is a teenage problem, or a slimmer's disease, a psychological issue, attention seeking, addiction - I have even heard people say that it is a trendy disorder to have! Far from it!

As an encouragement, I would like to say that eating disorders can be healed through prayers. This is a bold statement and I wouldn't presume to say that this is the only way to be cured, especially if the eating disorder has been a problem for many years. Although God can perform miracles and can heal instantly, a certain amount of change has to come from within before normal eating habits can be exercised and maintained.

God is gentle and understands all our inner feelings. He knows our needs, whether it is our own desire to be cured, or to help a friend or relative, but most of all the Lord is our Father and does not want us to suffer. It is His will that we be healed.

This book is my testimony, the journey starting with my life history to my freedom. My past cannot be re-written, but I believe the Lord wants me to use my experiences for good. I have had many prophecies over the last two years, which indicate that God is good and He would not want to hurt us. I hope you do get inspiration from this book, because God's seal of approval is written over all the pages. There is no intention to condemn, ridicule or persecute anyone - only to bless.

To begin with, we need to establish *why* we have an eating disorder: can we identify why it is we suffer from these abnormal eating patterns? Trace back over your life history. It may take weeks, or even months to open all the little doors of your past to establish where this problem started. It may have been triggered by a single event, or resulted from an accumulation of events, or it may be from circumstances beyond your control, or it may even be genetic - an inherited family trait.

Traumatic events can trigger something in your brain - divorce, death, physical/emotional/sexual abuse - look, too, at the happy times - weddings, births, celebrations. Look back very carefully at your life - write everything down, if it helps, then analyse your history.

THE WOMAN I ADMIRE MOST
(*My best friend*)

After I read Ella's book for the first time I cried, I was very upset for a couple of reasons, firstly because of the long terrible journey and struggle Ella had to take to free herself of all her demons.

Secondly for a very selfish reason I didn't know any of it. I realised thatI knew absolutely nothing about her, This hurt and made me very sad. My very special friend was like a stranger to me, why did I not know everything she had to go through.

The first time I clapped eyes on Ella it was her first day at our school, She was standing alone just outside of the girls toilets, arms folded and chewing and blowing bubbles with her gum. All the girls I was with looked over to her and said, "who does she think she is", I ignored their comments and went to say hi.

We were only really friends in school, reading about the things that happened out of school was a complete shock to me, I didn't know any of it. Yes she was a bit rebellious in school, I was too, but I didn't realise she was spiralling out of control. Once we left school we kept in touch, We fell pregnant at the same time our boys Joshua and Lewis were born 5 days apart, Then Daniel was born followed by my daughter Keira, we used to get together with the kids and everything to me seemed just fine, I had no idea about Ella's eating disorder.

I look back now and cringe at remembering when Ella used to come over, I would always offer her lunch, and she would always decline, and only had coffee, I remember admiring her for being able to refuse food, something I could never do. I remember saying to her once "how can you not eat lunch", and I would always comment on how lucky she was that she stayed so slim, she would sit and smile and say nothing, If only I had known I would never of been so insensitive. I wish she could have confided in me.

Ella didn't tell me for a long time that she had let Jesus into her life. I can only guess that she was concerned about my reactions as I am a non believer. It didn't matter to me Ella will always be a special friend, whatever.

I have seen the friends she surrounds herself with from the church, having a tight knit community is amazing, and speaking as a non believer it is a lovely thing to see.

Ella has always been a ray of sunshine to me, and has increasingly given more and more to others since joining the church. I am always in awe of her, she never fails to surprise me in things she does in life and all for the good of others. How she fits everything into her schedule I do not know.

I am so proud of her achievements, especially after sharing her struggles through life to the world with this book. I know things can only get better and better for Ella. I often tell her she needs to slow down and rest as she is always so busy with her work, But deep down I know this will probably never happen, her work is too important to her, and she will just keep giving to others, unselfishly.

Ella always makes me smile.
Ella is the woman I most admire.
Paula Lawson
(*My Best Friend*)

IN THE PAST

Well, as a school kid, I was always aware of the gang of girls, which Ella hung around with. I would keep my head down in the corridor, in case of mean remarks, or bullying tactics, played out on the younger pupils, like myself. Ella appeared 'hard as nails', dressed like a 'mod', and didn't take much rubbish from anyone! If I was to say that we were friends at school, it would be a lie! I was scared of Ella and kept well away!

In Ella's teenage years, I would often hear that Ella was 'in trouble again', through our parents friendship. I would witness times where our mothers would pray for a miracle, and for Ella to get to know a God, who loved her, and wanted her heart to be softened towards him.

Finally, prayers were answered! Ella entered the church doors, as a broken and hurting woman. When Ella became a Christian, she shared some of the devastating situations and trauma's she had gone through, as a girl and since running away from home.

It has been a road of recovery for Ella. She has changed from a teen, with a hard exterior, (in order to hide silent pain), to become a restored, secure woman, who knows God loves her. I believe God has, and will continue to use her experiences for a purpose…. to tell others about the healing love of Jesus.

Her love for children is amazing, and her gift in puppetry and children's ministry, has developed, from her desire to see children come to know Jesus, and be healed of hurts, which stop them receiving the fullness of God's joy and love.

Her friend Andrea Tuckwell XX

Living Behind the Mask

CONTENTS PAGE

Living Behind the Mask

Chapter 1

CHAPTER ONE

Back to the Roots

My parents had grown up together and went to the same school in a little mining village where everybody knew everyone. When my father left school, the career choice was the army or the pit! He hated the pit life and wanted to escape from Nottingham to make something of his life and travel the world.

I was born in 1970, in Plymouth, Devon. My father was in the armed forces, and my mother was alone a lot of the time, being a dutiful housewife and mother. My mum was alone when she gave birth to me and when, shortly after I was born, I developed pneumonia and bronchitis, my great-grandfather and great-grandmother took a taxi from Nottingham to Plymouth to help Mum care for this sick child. From the beginning, there was a strong bond between my great-grandmother and myself. It was as though this bond had built up whilst my mother carried me in her womb. When my father returned from an army exercise, they had me christened (I think because it was the proper thing to do).

We moved about a great deal because my dad was in the army. I don't think Mum realised at first that she would be married to my father's career.

We moved to Malta. Mum said I was a very intelligent little girl and, as children had to go to pre-school, by the age of two I not only knew my alphabet - but knew it backwards. I excelled in all my work. From photographs and stories told by my father I know they were a popular couple, parties would last all weekends, beer crates were stacked up to the ceiling, and the house was full of single soldiers who were like big brothers who protected me and bought me presents.

Mum needs people. Her mother had made her attend Sunday school when she was a child and Mum knew she would find friendships in a church, so when we moved back to Plymouth, she settled into a local Methodist Church. She made friends quickly and joined the local drama group, and I would go along with her to all the rehearsals.

My mother had the lead role in Mother Goose one year, and I would sit in the front row, sometimes alone, glued to my seat, watching my mother in awe. I was so proud. I could even recite the songs and a lot of the actors' lines.

When the curtain went up on the first evening, the whole place was packed full of people. I felt special and dreamed that one day I would be on a big stage. I sat there thinking, "That's my Mum!" It was wonderful - the costumes, the excitement of it all gave me such a buzz.

Our family had remained in Nottingham and we went to visit my grandparents there. My great-grandfather was a barber, with his own barber shop, so everyone in the village knew our family. A gentle man, he was deaf and walked with a stick. A mine had exploded near him in the war and had blown off half of his foot and also caused his deafness. I remember having to shout loud so that he could hear.

One time, when I ran into their old Victorian house, shouting and shouting for him, he didn't come. I ran into each room. He was usually in the piano room so I ran in there, but he was nowhere to be seen. I began to get frightened, and when I looked at the adult faces they bore sad, sympathetic expressions. He was dead! I cried myself to sleep for

Chapter 1

a long time after this, I was really hurting.

My other grandparents (Mum's parents) lived in a wonderful house, so different from the plain walled army quarters. They had a cool walk-in pantry full of food, and when I looked up to the shelves it was more like a mini supermarket. The smell of this room enchanted me, with the blue walls and stone floor adding to the coolness.

Grandma was such a loving woman, like an older version of Mum. She had a big green rocking chair in the corner of the kitchen under a large painted cupboard. All the grandchildren loved it, and I would rock backwards and forwards just watching my grandmother prepare the big meals. She would come and sit beside me and sing to me. Over and over again I would ask her to sing "My grandfather's clock is too tall for the shelf, etc. etc." It was my favourite song.

Just above this rocking chair was a big cupboard where my grandfather kept a tin and money boxes full of copper coins. He would fill up little money bags and give them out to the grandchildren - and there were lots of us.

I would race up the road with my bag of coins and call for my cousins on the way. They were a family of five children, and I desperately wanted to be part of their family - so many people to play with. My dad didn't like me going there, he was so strict. I wished desperately that I had a twin sister somewhere, and that one day Mum and Dad would produce her out of the cupboard. I felt that I had something missing in my life. I was a dreamer.

When I was five, we moved to Leeds where we lived in a cul-de-sac. Already I had so many memorised addresses in my head - different schools, different friends. Mum worked at a youth centre. I loved that place, and when Dad was away I was allowed to go with her. The flashing lights and loud music were awesome. Lots of the teenagers would buy me chocolate, and the girls would take me on to the dance floor and dance with me. I convinced myself that they thought I was older than I actually was and I felt very grown up. They probably didn't think this at all.

"*Brown Girl in the Ring*" by Boney M was the rage at the time. My mum bought the album for me and I was so proud of it. It was my first vinyl record, and there was a poster inside the album sleeve which I stuck on the wall. Mum gave me her old record player and a lot of old singles which I listened to again and again. This Boney M album really pricked my ears, especially "*By the Rivers of Babylon*." the words ring in my head even now -

> *"By the rivers of Babylon, where we sat down,*
> *Yeah we weep, when we remember Zion,*
> *Carry us away from captivity."*

It goes on, but these words in particular have stayed with me.

Mum also used to take me swimming every week, and afterwards we would have a chip butty and coke. I didn't like the swimming but looked forward to spending this time afterwards with my mum alone. She was such a lovely person, and so kind that I could never understand why she was always putting herself down about the way she looked, and how fat she was.

I had a budgie called "Smokey" - a special bird who was very intelligent. I trained him to talk, and we played together with my little

Chapter 1

dolls in the doll's house. Smokey would empty a match box and then pick the matchsticks up again and put them away - it was incredible what this bird could do. I couldn't bear to be separated from him.

Mum and I went to my grandparent's house one summer. You could smell the coal fires as you drove into the village. I loved staying there. I would get up early because I knew Grandma would be downstairs fixing the fires up for the day. She was all warm and cuddly in her fluffy pink dressing gown. She would sit me in the rocking chair and tell me stories of when I was very tiny, of how she would bathe me in her sink and wrap me up in a warm towel and lay me beside the roaring fire. She would tell stories of my mum and her brothers and sisters. It was so interesting and I always felt grown up when she shared these things with me.

On this particular visit, we took Smokey with us. I had been naughty and Mum threatened to let Smokey go if I wasn't a good girl. She took him outside to my grandfather's garden and I screamed for her to bring him back. My uncle saw this and thought he would tease me by doing the same thing. He took the bird outside again and - not maliciously, he was a practical joker - the bottom accidentally fell off the cage and my bird flew away. I ran upstairs and cried. While my uncle tried to console me, I overheard Mum saying that Smokey probably wouldn't survive in the wild. I was angry and sad, but later that day, to my delight, my uncle said he had found Smokey. I jumped up excitedly, so relieved and happy to see Smokey again. However, there was something different - maybe it was because my bird had been cold outside? It was the same blue colour and in the same cage.

When I took the bird out of the cage, it pecked me really hard, so I spoke to it, but it didn't speak back. I placed the little doll's pushchair in the cage, but it didn't push it. This was not my bird. I felt grief and had to accept that my bird was gone forever and that this bird was an intruder and would not replace Smokey.

I went into my room and cried most of the night. I looked out of my bedroom window where, from my grandparent's house, the lights illuminated the pit wheel, with the large slag heaps shadowed in the background.

Granddad's garden was a wonderful place. Grandma said he had green fingers, but I didn't quite know what that meant because his hands were always yellow.

He smoked a lot and had a pipe rack that smelled of stale tobacco. Granddad would spend most of his day either in his garden or in his greenhouse, nurturing his vegetables and flowers. He won a lot of prizes for his gardening gift The food tasted so rich, and although I didn't like vegetables, I had to eat them because they had been grown by hand. The garden had a different meaning for me from then on.

On this visit, I was thrilled to be asked to be a bridesmaid and was measured up for a bridesmaid's dress. My uncle and his girlfriend were getting married and I had never been to a wedding before. A few months later, we returned to Grandma's house for the wedding. I remember going to the bride's house, and it was such an exciting day, with everyone running around panicking. My cousin and myself were the youngest and we were playing together. She was to be a flower girl. We had our hair done and, although usually I looked so plain, I looked transformed when I put on the pretty blue dress. It was such a celebration, and we were photographed every time we turned our heads. I hated having my photograph taken because I didn't like looking at myself. The day was long and finished with flashing lights and loud music in a big hall.

I also stayed a lot with my great-grandmother who used to tell me that I was her favourite, and that she had no time for the other children. Everything smelled old in her house: the tables and chairs were large and chunky, and there was always a loaf of uncut bread on the table, with a large sharp chopping knife lying beside it. She would spread beef dripping on the top end, then slice the bread very thinly after she had pasted it. This fascinated me.

I slept in my great-grandmother's huge bed - it was a lot bigger than my parent's bed and had masses of pillows and blankets. If I lay flat under the covers and hid, my grandmother couldn't see me, and she would fall for this trick every time - or at least I thought she did. The bed was warm, but once, when Grandma put a hot water bottle made of pot in the bed, it cracked and soaked the bed.

She had such funny things in her house: there was a cotton spinning wheel, a treadle sewing machine, and she even had a chamber pot under the bed, like a large teacup, which she used as a toilet in the middle of the night.

I lived in a fantasy world and loved to watch people dancing on the television, and listening to music. Great-grandma would encourage my imagination, saying I was a special girl, and she would tell me how she had special powers which I could have. I dreamed of becoming a dancer, and attended ballet and tap dancing school, which was really good fun. I was one of the youngest pupils and thought the older girls were so good. I loved the ballet shoes, they were so feminine, and when I stood on my tiptoes I was so tall.

Living Behind the Mask

When we returned home, it was back to school and back to normality until one day I arrived home to find a pile of khaki clothes on the kitchen floor and a sweaty, damp, musty smell lingering throughout the house. My father was in the lounge, all fresh and clean. He played with me on the floor, tickling me until my sides hurt. I can't remember laughing so much and thought how great it would be if this was how it was going to be. I wouldn't mind his staying at home forever.

The house was spotless but Mum seemed to be on edge, as she always was when Dad came home. This was the longest time that my dad had spent at home so far in my life. Before this, I thought "Daddy" was a letter more than a person. Fathers were only part-time and when they did come home they were angry.

I joined the maypole dancers at school. I had a pretty white dress with a blue and red sash. We practised for months and, on the school's Open Day, the dancing team danced around the maypole. Mum and Dad were in the crowd, and we had strict instructions not to wave to our parents, but I beamed the biggest smile over to them. I felt important and did all my moves perfectly.

During this time, a teenage boy took an unnatural interest in me. He didn't have any friends that I knew of and he took me for walks, then started playing with me in a way which made me very uncomfortable. He told me not to say anything to anyone or we would get into a lot of trouble, but that I must just tell him everything. There were two army blankets, a blue one and an orange one, that my mum let me play with and I hated them after a while. I don't feel it to be necessary to go into any details. I was now six, but my thoughts were way beyond my years. I knew that the way this boy touched and kissed me was wrong, but I was taught not to answer back to older people - and to me he was a male adult!

I gave up dancing because I did not like the thought of being weak: women were weak, men and boys were strong. I became clumsy and lost my co-ordination. This was probably deliberate, and I dropped out of dance school soon after. I still lived very much in my daydream world. I even convinced myself I could fly because I had seen on some television programme that if you believed in something strongly enough you would be able to do it, so there were many attempts to fly down the stairs, encouraged by the film *Peter Pan*.

I wasn't getting as much attention as I used to. Mum was getting fat and we stopped going swimming. Maybe the chip butties did this to you, I thought.

Mum was quite poorly. Dad painted my bedroom yellow. The first coat was very thin and the pale blue paint showed through, so Dad painted a picture of a man behind bars, just for fun. I lay in my double bed, drowned by all the blankets. The room was huge and the smell of paint was giving me a headache, but eventually I went to sleep.

I started experiencing nightmares at this point which carried on throughout my childhood. I dreamed that under my bed were hundreds and thousands of evil heads which, if they got hold of a person, ate them alive! I remember trying to scream, but I was dumb, and the heads were eating people all over the world. I woke up feeling very scared. The bedroom did not have any curtains up because of the decorating, and the street lamp shone through the window, illuminating the jailed man on the wall. I went into my parent's room to find it dark and the bed was still made, not even crumpled.

I put on my slippers, thinking they must be downstairs, but there was no light under the lounge door. I opened the door, and the room was empty. I was in complete darkness.

The front door was locked, so I ran to the kitchen, but that was locked, too. The linen basket lay in the middle of the kitchen floor, and I tipped out the contents and stood on the basket, climbed onto the stainless steel draining board, then opened the kitchen window. I looked down - it was a long way down. I shut my eyes and jumped, then ran to the next door neighbour's house to see if they were there.

The sky was black, but filled with thousands of stars - it looked beautiful. My friend's father answered the door and said that my parents were not there, but that I could share the bed with my friend. I snuggled up to her and felt very safe, and soon went into a deep sleep and, because I felt secure, I had no nightmares. Mum came round the next morning. Apparently they had been having a drink with friends across the road and had been checking on me every half hour. They had panicked when they found that I wasn't there, and had searched everywhere. Our neighbours told Mum I was there and could stay, and that there was no need to wake me now that I was asleep.

There was a shortage of water because we were facing a drought, but my perception of what 'drought' meant was distorted. I knew that we had to be very economical with our consumption of water, so I was careful not to waste any. The sun was very hot, and Mum noticed a white patch on my back which spread over my body. I went to the doctors' surgery but they couldn't diagnose what it was.

Soon after, my father said we would be going very early in the morning to Grandma's. It was an adventure - it seemed like the middle of the night because it was still dark, and it was just me and my dad. I felt very special as he let me sit in the front of the car, with all the streets illuminated with different coloured lights, and we went through tunnels and over bridges.

I stayed awake the whole time. Usually I sat in the back and was told to go to sleep, and I was usually travel sick, which seemed to aggravate my parents.

They would have to stop and clean me up, the car would smell of sick, and I would feel awful. Today, Dad listened to what I had to say and he didn't tell me to be quiet. I didn't understand what was happening, but it was good, it was a fresh morning and the chimneys were puffing away, and I could smell the burning of coal in the air. Grandma greeted us at the gate with open arms, then my Dad had a cup of tea and left me there.

A few days later, we travelled home but, on the way, we went to the hospital. I was not allowed to see Mum there, but when she came home she had a baby with her. My brother!

I remember Mum was in the bath, and Dad was sitting on the side of the bath when I went to the toilet. I was sore around my genitals, and Dad started to question me (he must have seen the pain on my face). I told him what was happening with the boy down the road and he asked Mum about it, but she said there was nothing in it. This was the point in time when I started to block my emotions, and did not want to open up. I felt that they thought I was a liar and that what I said didn't count. Or maybe these things were normal?

My parents bought me a hamster and I called it "Hammy". I used to talk to the hamster, it never judged me, and was always there to listen - and it loved me. I carried it in my pocket and I thought it liked being with me. It was my protector. One day, I wanted to treat my hamster, so I gave it a ride on the fence around our garden. I had to hold it and help it balance, and I didn't want to hurt it, but the fence was high and a long way round. When I got to the end of the fence, the hamster wasn't moving - I had killed it by smothering it with kindness. I went into the house screaming for Dad to bring it back to life. He flushed it down the toilet and I grieved in silence as I witnessed this. They replaced him with more hamsters who had babies, who had babies, so soon there were loads of them - so many that they started to eat each other and this horrified me. I didn't like hamsters at this point.

My brother Joseph was receiving so much attention that I resented him, and when I needed my parents the baby was crying or being fed. My dad was spending so much time with this child and I had never had this time because he was always away when I was younger. The focus was not on me any longer and I felt worthless, unable to talk as I was afraid that what I might have to say would be thought of as naughty or unacceptable.

The drought passed and then the heavens opened - it rained constantly. The thunder storms were scary and we spent a lot of break-times at school indoors, watching television, playing in the corridors amongst the wet coats, or drawing pictures. I liked drawing because it made me feel that I was good at something.

One break-time, the thunder was terrible and it felt like the whole school was shaking. There was a tar roof, and one of the older boys said that lightning can strike and set things alight, especially tar, and

Chapter 1

that was how men on the side of the road got red hot tar - they lay it on the road and it goes cold.

I was so gullible and sat in total horror waiting for the school to burn me alive, thinking that maybe I deserved to die!

As I sat in the cloakroom with my fists clenched tight and my eyes squeezed shut, I could hear the rumbles of thunder, so I put my coat over my face. There were some children playing noisily in the corridor, and suddenly there was an almighty scream. Oh no! One of my friends had been struck by lightning!

I was all right, so I must help. I looked from under my coat to see my friend standing there clutching her eyes. Beside her, a boy dropped the umbrella he held in his hand and ran when he saw the blood trickle through her fingers. I jumped up, forgetting about the darkness around and put my arm around her and, thinking that it was her hand which had been hurt, but as I pulled it down from her face I saw that it wasn't her hand that was bleeding - the point from the umbrella had speared her eyeball. I felt sick and took her to the teacher, but she never came back to school. I blamed myself. I could have stopped the fighting if I hadn't been such a coward. From now on, I must face things and be strong.

In school I was involved in recorder playing, and when we had a big concert I looked for my parents in the big crowd, but they weren't there. The play was all about rainbows and the promise that God gave to Noah. I wanted so much to be in that rainbow. The music teacher tried to encourage me to play the cello, but I didn't see why I should bother as I was always told not to play my recorder at home because it made a terrible noise and might wake Joseph.

I felt very rejected, and decided to take the burden of having me from them, not to punish them, It was just that I felt my time was at an end with my mum and dad and that they did not want me any longer. I ran away, taking a small case with a few possessions and a drink, but I only got to the park around the corner. I looked for a four leaf clover in the field, but I was not lucky and could never find them, then I sat on a log which was covered in green slimy algae which made it dangerous to walk on, but I tried, balancing myself with my arms outstretched and placing one foot in front of the other.

I was alone in the park and, although it was a summer's day, it was getting cooler. I hung upside down on the climbing frame but slipped and hit my head on the concrete, I had a dizzy feeling then felt a wetness on my head, and when I looked at my hand it was covered in blood. I freaked out and ran home. My mum screamed as she stood in the front doorway - they hadn't even noticed I had been missing. What had been the point? I had stayed away most of the day but no-one had realised. I went to the army medical centre where they gave me the all-clear.

My schoolwork was deteriorating and when I brought home my third bad school report, I hid behind a chair and waited for my dad to come in. To my surprise, he just sat me down and had a long talk with me. There was no shouting this time, he spoke softly and said he was puzzled because he could not understand why I had slipped so far behind. I didn't know the answers.

When I was seven, we moved to Germany into a block of flats. It was a big flat with a balcony, and it had huge storage spaces in the cellar and the attic which were great places for hiding and playing because they were soundproof, but very cold in the winter and like a sauna in the summer.

Chapter 1

My dad showed me how to develop my own photographs and I loved this because Joseph was too young to be involved and I received one-to-one attention from my father.

I followed Mum around like a lost sheep. I was seven but going on fourteen. I felt different, so much older than the other girls of my age, and very mature and independent. In the school holidays I felt special because I would be with Mum when she cleaned for the army in the army blocks, and it was so exciting. I would sit and listen to her and her friends talking, and their conversation fascinated me, but I didn't have anything worth saying - maybe I was stupid!

I started another school, and although all my friends had gone to a different one, I made friends quickly. I had an excellent English teacher who took a shine to me He encouraged me and spent a lot of time teaching me calligraphy. I excelled in this subject, but there was a black girl called Christy who resented me. She played with us in the playground but there was something sly about her.

I was quite a tomboy and the boys in the school let me join in their games. One day when we were playing catch-the-ball in the playground everyone seemed to be missing Christy out, so when I caught the ball I threw it to her, but instead of catching it, she misjudged it and it hit her in the face. The smack sent shivers through me. A rage came over her and she raced towards me, her eyes blazing fires, and she grabbed my hair and yanked it so hard that she ripped a huge clump of it from my scalp. It wasn't very long but there was enough for her to grab hold of.

The dinner lady ran over as I crouched, clutching my head. The girl had a smug grin on her face and she had the clump of hair still clutched in her fist. I could feel her piercing eyes burning holes through my body. As the dinner lady looked in horror at the bald patch on the back of my head, I passed out with the shock.

They sent for my mother. When she saw my head she was shaking and didn't know what to do so she took me to the medical centre. The doctor there said that he wasn't sure whether the hair would grow back, and that the shock could stop re-growth, but we must wait and see. I didn't want to go to school, afraid that the other children would make fun of me because, as the infants' class, we had to sit at the front of the hall in assemblies and I was worried about who would be sitting behind me. Luckily, the hair did grow back, eventually!

Christy and myself eventually became friends. I forgave her, but was still scared of her quick temper. One day we were playing in the park on the see-saw when I realised that I was a lot heavier than she was. I was really upset, thinking I was going to get fatter and fatter - and fat means ugly and unacceptable. I didn't want to be like that and I went home and weighed myself, becoming paranoid: I was four and a half stone.

I remember that when the school photographer came I would suck in my cheeks so that they didn't look so chubby, My hair was cut into a bob which made my features even more rounded and I hated looking at myself in the mirror, thinking that I was so ugly, and I became very introverted and shy. Some of the other children called me names because my skin condition had manifested as two symmetrical patches - one over each eye. The children called me names like 'Patch the Dog', or 'Panda' or 'Ella the Elephant'. I hated it - Was I an animal? Was I a freak? I knew I was different, but why?

I got involved in many activities but never felt good enough. I started learning how to play the guitar, but the music teacher didn't like me, so I dropped out. I appeared in a few plays at school - Oliver Twist, Jonah and the Whale, David and Goliath. I loved acting because I could be someone else - I didn't have to be myself.

By this time, the skin problem was spreading all over my body and, being tanned, the ivory patches were highlighted on my legs, arms, stomach, back and neck. I was so self-conscious and embarrassed by it. I knew that I was different and that this problem was worsening. I went to a specialist in a big German hospital where they diagnosed me as having Vitiligo - a skin disorder which destroys the pigments in the skin. There was no cure, so he prescribed various creams and suggested that I use ultra-violet lamps, but nothing worked. The children at school started to call me names - children can be so cruel. I was given some make-up to put on the patches, but it only made the white patches look orange.

We went on holiday each year, a few times to the seaside with the rest of the family, i.e. all my uncles, aunts, cousins, Grandma and Granddad. There was a sense of unity, and everyone was happy.

All the children would group together and we would have great fun, playing grown-up games like Bingo.

Once, when we went past the bingo place, I saw my other grandparents (Dad's parents) through the big glass windows. I waved to them and was just about to run to the door to see them when my grandmother gave me an evil look then turned the other way. She was such a horrible woman, but my grandfather was a gentle giant, Dad came from a family of ten, but his mother didn't seem to have an ounce of love inside her. From that moment on I never wanted to visit them again.

Living Behind the Mask

We returned to Germany. One of Mum's friends had a daughter who was a lot older than me, Trudy, who was in senior school but who didn't have any friends. She took an interest in me and at first it made me feel special, but things changed when she started bribing me to let her touch me and made me touch her. This moved onto other things. Most of this abuse took place in the large attic. It makes my stomach turn even to think of it now and I feel it is not necessary to go into details, but this lasted for a period of about six months.

I was too terrified to tell anyone.

Trudy had a little pewter Irish leprechaun and she said that if I told anyone what happened she would throw this evil looking figure into the fire and it would come alive, and when it came alive it would come and kill me. My fear of the evil heads under my bed returned in my dreams - all the heads had the same face as the leprechaun.

On the days when the abuse took place, I would hibernate afterwards in my bedroom. I had a bed which was connected to shelving of a German design, with sliding padded green compartments behind which I stored all my secret possessions. I would jam my head against these and stick my nose in the gap between the bed and the unit. The fresh smell of pine gave me great comfort, and there was a cool breeze from under the bed and, although it was such a hot summer and the attic was so hot, I felt free there.

I was not a thumb sucker, but I would find myself biting furiously on my thumb until there were teeth imprints on it. If I was disturbed, I would make the excuse that I was tired, or sit up and read., I couldn't tell anyone, but wished over and over again that someone would guess what was happening so that the leprechaun wouldn't kill me. I felt I must be a really horrid person for this to happen again - this wasn't normal and I hated myself. My trust in people had been destroyed.

When my mother became a Christian soon after this, all her friends persecuted her and she was an outcast from the other army wives. I was not even allowed to play with some of my friends because of Mum's beliefs. Mum and Dad argued. Mum was very snappy - she had given up drinking and smoking. My dad was drinking very heavily at this point and had lost his driving licence so Mum had to drive him everywhere. Dad hated this because he didn't like the way Mum drove. Then he was court marshalled. It was a really depressing time.

There was a sense of freedom about the winters in Germany. I really enjoyed them - snow and ice made it like a fairytale. There was a pond nearby where we would take our ice skates and lose ourselves for hours. My Dad would take Joseph and myself out on the sledge and it was good fun, but I always felt shy if I saw anyone I knew. A blanket of snow lay across the land.

Joseph started playschool. He hated it because he didn't want to be separated from Mum, and she was heartbroken when she had to leave him. I was almost glad Joseph was made to go. I was off school a lot, always having tonsillitis and being ill. Sometimes I would fake it just to keep away from school and stay at home and get the attention from Mum. Also, I could sit and listen to Mum talk with her friends, which made me feel grown up.
Mum continued to be rejected by her so-called-friends, but she found new friends in the church. We were forced to go and I hated Sunday school, it was so boring. This God which Mum had now found was taking her away from the family. She was so happy but didn't have

any time for me and she went to bible study, prayer evenings, church meetings, etc.

We were restricted where we were because we lived in a German community. I thrived on danger and would go into an old boarded up house to play. Nearby, there was a supermarket and, with my friends, I would go in and we would steal sweets, then take them back to our hide-out - it was our secret.

I remember that once the family went to the local ice-cream parlour and Joseph fainted due to the coldness of the ice-cream. I took delight in seeing my dad panic as he tried to explain in his broken German to the man behind the counter that he wanted water. The man was puzzled and my father pushed him aside aggressively as he grabbed handfuls of water from the tap and threw it over my brother's face. To my disappointment, he came round. I wasn't purposely resentful of Joseph because deep down I did love him, but I longed to be loved by my parents in the way that they loved him and showed him that they did.

The next time Mum, Joseph and myself visited this ice-cream parlour, I watched in anticipation for him to faint again, but he didn't. As I looked out onto the busy street, though, to my horror, a little boy was run over by a bus. There was such a commotion as the street filled with ambulances, police cars and traffic jams. The boy was about the same age as my brother. I felt a pain in my chest and was aware of an un-customary compassion for Joseph. This image stayed with me for years.

We moved out of the flats into a house on the army barracks. It was a big house and we were lucky to get it because there were only four houses on the whole estate. I moved school again, but at least I had got away from Trudy. My bedroom was different and I hated it. Mum and Dad had sold my bedroom suite so my security was gone and I didn't sleep properly for months.

Dad had his driving licence back and we went on camping holidays with friends. Dad had injured his back a few years previously while pole vaulting and he had had to surrender most of his sports - a detriment to his army career as a skilful sportsman is commended for his ability.

My dad got very frustrated in his pain and was abusive to all around. Mum was not the best of map readers and he always blamed her for getting us lost. He would shout at me for not looking happy and would tell me to cheer up, saying I was a miserable, ungrateful little sod!

At the dinner table, I had developed an itching nose. I would get very nervous, especially if my dad was looking at me, and scratch the end of my nose. Then I would eat another mouthful, and the prickle would start again. My father would say angrily that I was doing it on purpose just to provoke him. The itching became habitual each mealtime and Mum would scold me for making my dad angry, but I wasn't inventing it, it was just as aggravating for me as it was for everyone else. I felt so on edge.

I started to take delight in teasing Joseph and domineering him. I took pleasure in playing games with him where I was in total control, for example, when I played the Mum and we called Joseph "Baby Bobby", I would make up bowl after bowl of Readybrek, giving him one spoonful, then me one spoonful. He would say he had had enough, but I would force him to eat it and this gave me the excuse to eat, too, and I would finish off the bowl.

They bought us a dog. I had pestered my parents for years, so they got a King Charles Cavalier spaniel, called Benji, then got his brother,

Benson. I played a game called 'Slave' with my brother, where I was the master and he was the slave and I would tie the dog's lead around his neck and lead him round everywhere like a dog. I would give him treats to reward him for doing something for me and I would eat something every time I gave him a treat.

When I think back, it was a horrible game. We would go through spoonfuls of peanut butter and chocolate spread. Yuck! I never admitted that I was the culprit, even when my mum confronted me.

I started horse riding and loved it. I could lose myself on the horse and it gave me a buzz - a horse cannot judge you, is obedient and gives pleasure and I loved the wonderful feeling of power that came from being so high up.

This was my escape from my father's strictness and I needed to get away from him, from the really hurtful things he would say. I felt worthless around him.

When I went on a skiing holiday without my parents, it was wonderful, I was free! The trip was to Bavaria, and I had so much attention that I wished I would never have to go home again. I got a silver medal for coming second over the whole week's skiing, and there was such a sense of adventure, my mischievous character came out this week. There were a couple of boys interested in me. I remember sending a postcard, but not phoning home, and I was upset to be returning home.

I took my eleven plus and passed with distinction, so I had the option of going to grammar school. I desperately wanted to get away because, by this time, I was absolutely terrified of my father. I asked if I could go to boarding school, seeing it as a means of getting away. One of my

Chapter 1

friends went to boarding school and she only came home at holiday times - I envied her freedom.

My parents brought me back to England and, as Mum and Dad couldn't afford for me to fly back to Germany every term holiday, it was agreed that I could stay at my grandmother's house. We looked round a former 'all boys' school where they were starting to enrol some girls, and the whole building was fascinating - huge and old. We looked around the dormitories and the girls there seemed such sissies that I felt a sense of power. I was getting a lot of attention and I loved it.

We returned home because the placements were few and the building of the dormitories for the girls hadn't been completed - obviously they had to be separated from the boys. The entrance exams were difficult and would determine whether I would go to the local secondary school or the boarding school.

The results came through during the summer holiday. I had failed the mark. I was distraught and remember crying silently on my bed.

I always had a sense of knowing things before they actually happened. My great-grandmother said I had the gift of seeing things in the future, and this grew stronger and stronger as I got older. It was quite frightening sometimes and I was afraid to tell anyone.

I began to think I must have been adopted - yes, that's right - one day my real parents would come to rescue me and take me away. It would be such a perfect family, myself and my twin sister.

Living Behind the Mask

CHAPTER TWO

Growing up is so confusing

Term started. It was my first day at secondary school, a massive building, and there were even guards on the gates with guns - it was like a prison! I hated it. There were so many big children and they looked like adults to me. The work was hard, the teachers were strict, there were so many rules and regulations, and we had to wear a uniform which was old fashioned.

I especially hated Physical Education. I hated my body, which was ugly and abnormal, the patches were severe and infested my body, and I was more developed than other girls in my year, especially my chest. I would make excuses as to why I couldn't do P.E. to avoid the showers, but the teacher would force me into the showers with the rest of the girls. I was so ashamed that I even tried going in fully-clothed so that no-one could see my freakish body, but this attracted even more attention when I was scolded. Although I loved netball and hockey, I still got my mum to write sick notes.

I particularly hated cross-country running, and on Sports Day the boys were chanting "Boing, Boing, Boing!" as they watched my chest as it bounced up and down when I ran, I was so sensitive because I felt flabby and was desperate to do something about it. I went on an egg diet for a week, but I didn't lose weight and only made myself unwell, with overwhelming cramping pains in my stomach.

I was still tormenting my brother, especially now that I had to take him with me everywhere I went.

Living Behind the Mask

It was Halloween night and we were going trick-or-treating with some of my friends. People were very generous and we got bags full of treats and money. I used Joseph to knock on the door, with his little lantern in one hand, and when the door opened, out we would pop. Then disaster struck. As we were going round a block of flats, Joseph's lantern burst into flames, and as he swung it round in an attempt to extinguish the flames, he caught the banisters and they became engulfed in flames. Luckily they were made of metal and plastic, so the blaze was easily controlled, but the melted mass smelt awful.

Joseph was in shock and, remembering the fright I saw in his eyes, I used this fear when I wanted something - I would bribe him to get me things or threaten to burn the banisters. I was a horrible sister!

My dad was also giving my brother a particularly hard time. He was trying to teach him his times tables, and would spend each night going over and over them. Joseph frequently ended in tears because he couldn't grasp them and my dad would be in a bad temper for the rest of the evening.

My dad would verbally abuse the whole family and he could make the nicest day turn into a nightmare, I would sometimes go to bed feeling totally useless, a complete failure. I was so weary of his negative comments that I would ask my father to hit me, for at least then it would only hurt initially and eventually wear off and perhaps this would release my Dad's anger. But no, he preferred to stab at me with aggressive insulting words, then twist them round and round until I was confused as to what the issue had been in the beginning. Was this obsessive exaggeration of expression actually necessary? Obviously it was!

I would absorb all these words like a sponge, believing the things he said about me and that I must be a dreadful girl, unworthy of love. I don't recall any of my friends saying their parents treated them in this way. In the playground I heard other children singing a ditty "Sticks and stones will break my bones, but names will never hurt me" - how wrong that was!

I developed a cough which developed into whooping cough and I had to spend months in bed. I couldn't eat, and when I tried, I coughed myself sick, and when I started walking again, I couldn't exert myself because it set me off whooping.

I had lost a lot of weight in the six months that I had been ill, and when I returned to school this attracted a lot of attention from my classmates who remarked on how thin I was. I liked this attention, and the fact that my clothes were big for me.

Many things had changed in school during those six months and people were a lot more cliquey, making it difficult for me to be included.

At break times I would go to the library alone and read books, and in the lessons I would sit at the back and hold back from coughing to avoid the embarrassment.

Due to my illness, Mum had left her part-time job in the thrift shop, but then started working at school as the lady who collected the dinner money. I was embarrassed by this and tried to avoid talking to her when my friends were around. She was determined that I would eat properly because I had lost so much weight during my illness, but I was equally determined to stay thin. I would walk around sucking in my stomach and started exercising, as Mum did when she thought she had gained too much weight.

Living Behind the Mask

Because it was my first year at school, I had missed out on sex education and was quite naive about things. When Mum asked me if I knew about the birds and the bees, I thought, because of what had happened in my earlier years, that I did, so she didn't tell me anything.

When I started my periods I was scared, and I thought I had cut myself, but it wouldn't stop bleeding, so I had to tell my mum, but she only laughed and said I had nothing to worry about, assuming that I knew this would happen. I went along with it, but was shocked when she gave me some tampons and I read the instructions on the box. I felt like crying because the pain in my stomach was so intense, and when I overheard Mum telling one of her friends I was now a woman, I felt betrayed. I couldn't trust anyone.

My parents paid for me to go on a summer camp which was a great experience. We went hiking, rock climbing, abseiling, canoeing and had a really fun time. We roamed about at night, sneaking into each other's tents until we got caught and all got the cane.

The best experience of all was sitting around the fire toasting crumpets and singing songs. My confidence was strong and I didn't want to go home.

Most of my spare time was spent at the garrison swimming pool where a lot of the boys thought I was a lot older than I was and I got a lot of attention. Everyone knew me because when I cut my foot when I dived in and had to go for stitches, I had bravely gone alone and hadn't needed my parents. My parents were shocked when they came home and found me with my foot all bandaged up and resting on a chair.

My best friend at this time was going through confirmation with her church. She spoke fluent German because, although her father was Scottish, her mother was German, and the accents of both of her parents fascinated me. She was an only child and got lots of attention from her parents. I thought again that I must have been adopted because why didn't they give me this kind of attention? There were no angry words, just praise, and I loved spending time at my friend's house. Again I fantasized about having a sister and how we would be inseparable.

At this time, my dad went on an exercise to the UK which allowed a bonding time for my mum and myself. He seemed to be away for a long time. One day, Mum sat me down and told me that something awful had happened - Dad was in hospital. She didn't tell me the full story at this time, but I found out later that he had been drunk in a pub and had been showing off when some youths had ganged up on him in the toilets and beaten him up badly. He was having his face rebuilt and we didn't even speak to him for months because he couldn't talk. His jaw was restructured and when he did return home eventually, he was different - he was kind, he stopped smoking, and vowed never to drink again.

I started going out with boys a lot older than myself because I felt that boys of my own age were childish. I started experimenting sexually at an early age and felt that I had experience, but really just longed to be loved - to be held.

I became self-conscious about my image as a person and didn't like myself very much and didn't feel that anyone really liked me. I had one very good friend, William, who was a lot older than I was. A popular boy, he was my protector, and I wasn't attracted to him but regarded him more as a big brother. I wasn't aware at the time of how much he cared for me.

My dad took up windsurfing and encouraged me to join him in his new interest. It was brilliant, Dad was showing an interest in me, spending one-to-one time with just me, and we laughed and played together. We wore wetsuits that made me look fat. I was so plain and podgy looking. It wasn't all smooth going, though. One day my watch fell into the water, never to be seen again, and my father scolded me and I felt terrible because I hadn't done it on purpose.

We had a big cellar where we stored our windsurfers and where I even had a room to myself, carpeted, where I could play my music as loud as I wanted. I could lock myself away and lose myself in my thoughts. I had feelings that I would die at an early age and found myself wishing that I would live until I was 30 - at that age 30 seemed old. I would speak to Mum's God and ask if he would help me to keep my teeth until I was at least 20. This sounds silly now, but these were some of the horrible thoughts I had in the middle of the night.

I was doing well at school but was becoming even more introverted. One of Mum's friends was a teacher at school and she spent a lot of time on me, which embarrassed me because I didn't want to be seen to be the teacher's pet. I didn't really like this teacher who was a Christian, so I picked up typing very quickly, knowing that if I did well I could get out of her class.

I began experimenting with alcohol to see what the attraction was. We always had drink in the house so, when my parents went out, some of my friends came round and we got into the drinks cabinet, trying one drink after another. It was horrible and the taste of whisky burnt my throat, but I felt a happiness and I liked this feeling. I was 12 years old.

My dad had started drinking again but he was always a lovely person the day after a heavy drinking bout, especially if he had been particularly nasty the day before. He could also be a prankster and make people laugh, but when he played tricks on us sometimes I was intimidated and felt he was laughing at me and found this humiliating.

We continued to go to the garrison swimming pool but I started to cover myself up, trying to hide my body because my top half was becoming more pronounced. A group of soldiers, who seemed to us to be really old, started chatting up my friends and myself but we weren't interested. They obviously didn't realise how old I was and a few days later they were astonished when I went into the army mess with my dad, their senior, and they never bothered us again. I felt protected.

Whilst in Germany, we visited the concentration camp at Belsen. It was a desolate, icy, hostile place, and even the birds hovering above gave it an eerie feeling. The silence was deafening and I related to this because I was becoming so isolated in my life and I felt a real sense of loneliness.

I tried different diets and read Mum's diet books in secret. My self-esteem was low.

I was too embarrassed to bring friends home and reveal Mum's fanaticism about her Christianity. We had posters all over the house which made me cringe: in the toilet...

"For God so loved the world that He gave His only begotten son that whomsoever believeth in Him should not perish but have everlasting life",

... and in the kitchen...

"I stand at the door and knock if anyone hears my voice and opens the door, I will come into him and will sup with him and he with me".

Living Behind the Mask

I seized every opportunity to stay away at friends' houses, but very rarely would I have them back to our house. There was one girl, Mum's best friend's daughter, who understood. Claire was a plump girl, who was always trying to lose weight, and I liked her, but her passion for food probably didn't do me any good. At every opportunity we would bake cakes, cookies - anything. Her mum allowed us to make a mess of the kitchen if we cleaned up afterwards, and she would keep out of our way (probably the best thing!).

Mum and Dad argued, and I think it might have been because he was in trouble for Mum's involvement in the church she was attending. The army life was so restricting for wives, and I vowed I would not get involved with a soldier, although I thought I would like to be one myself when I was older - soldiers had such power over people, and I had had enough of being powerless.

Somehow I survived until the age of thirteen when Dad had the chance of a posting to England and my dream had come true. I didn't want to be in Germany any more. My parents gave me the choice of whether to stay or go, saying that whatever I wanted they would do. This was such a grown up decision - I could make new friends, start a new school, get rid of my depression! Yes, we would go - a fresh start.

We moved to Colchester and I realised that this was one of the biggest mistakes of my life. We moved into brand-new army quarters and I started a new school where I had no friends.

On the first day I was sexually harassed by boys and bullied by girls. The school didn't seem to have any discipline, there was no real school uniform, and everyone seemed to do what they pleased. There was a group of girls who congregated in the toilets and smoked, and they made it clear that this was their patch. I was the new girl who they didn't like, and I knew I would have to prove myself.

One kind girl, Paula, did talk to me. I didn't realise it at the time but she was to be my lifelong friend. What had I done? I had made a mistake. There was no turning back, and I couldn't tell my parents that I didn't like the school, they would be so angry because it had been such a disruption moving countries. I went home and felt sorry for myself.

I made friends with some boys, skinheads, who said they would look after me, and when two girls took an instant dislike to me, the two boys said I should show them who was boss and not let them bully me. The girls persisted, though, until finally the name-calling and pushing in the corridor made me see red. Why should I be pushed around? I told these girls I would meet them outside after school and we could sort it out, and they both laughed in my face.

Revenge was mine because one of the boys made a metal rod in metalwork, sneaked it out and put this evil weapon into the palm of my hand. I clutched it tight as I confronted them and, as the word had got round the school, saw that there was a crowd gathering. Although I was scared, I couldn't let these people down - they had come for some entertainment - so I started pushing the girls around. One ran off, and the other was scared stiff, so I started laying into her. I couldn't believe my strength and, as the two skinheads shouted my praise, I felt important and full of power. Everyone was shouting for me, then suddenly they all scattered as the head teacher got hold of me and the other girl and dragged us back into school. The events of my first week at the new school resulted in my being suspended for the second week.

My dad was furious, and shouted that he couldn't understand my behaviour and that it had caused him embarrassment. I was banned from going out of the house and when the boys came to call for me, my dad rounded on me again, demanding to know what was happening to me and telling me that the boys must stay away from the house and that they were bad news.

I argued that he didn't know them, he wasn't being fair, he was taking them at face value, and he wasn't giving them a chance. This made him even more mad because I had never answered him back before.

When I returned to school, everyone knew me as the new girl who was a heroine, and everyone wanted to be my friend. I started to go out with one of the skinheads, I skipped school, spent my dinner money on cigarettes, went up town and got into more and more trouble. On the days when I was at school I would take charge and bully other children and encourage other pupils to threaten the people who were trying desperately to avoid our gang. We would throw chewing gum in their hair, kick them, punch them, take their school bags and throw them to each other, we would throw eggs and stones at them, destroy their work, and steal workbooks and copy them.   It got bad when I was not afraid of anyone - I could even reduce the teachers to tears through verbal abuse and the nasty tricks we played on them. A boy in our year stuffed himself with food and then made himself sick into a carrier bag, and we tipped this over other kids' heads.

When one of the temporary teachers couldn't stand my abuse any longer and ran out of the room crying, I laughed and encouraged everyone else in the classroom to join in with the torment. My religious education teacher spoke to me and said that he was worried about me and that he wasn't sleeping, but waking in the middle of the night thinking of me. He said Jesus was watching me and He knew that I was in pain. I laughed in this mans' face and, when I told my friends what he had said, we tormented him. I was sent to the head teacher on many occasions and put in the special room for disobedient pupils. The head of department summoned me to his room and told me I was a waster and would make nothing of my life, and that I might as well go home.

A couple of months later an orange van started following me to school and the man driving it asked if I would like a lift, and that he would take me to Clacton. He said that he knew that I didn't like school and that he had been watching me. He was unkempt, with scruffy hair and dirty stubble on his face. I tried to get away but he kept following, and this went on for weeks until I plucked up the courage to tell a teacher.

The police were involved and I had a police escort to school each day. My dad was confused as to why I hadn't told him about this, but it was because I was too scared, and I didn't talk to my parents that much by this point anyhow, thinking that they wouldn't understand. The police caught the man and charged him. Could I still have fear inside me?

My dad made comments about my fat bottom and my clothes being tight - I was up to eleven and a half stone. He said that my hair was a mess and needed to be cut and that I had to do something about it. I was hurt and took a good look at myself. I was fat and I needed to do something about it. I would show him I could do it. I heard all the comments he made to Mum and I didn't want this criticism.

I remembered how much weight I had lost when I had whooping cough and how good I had looked then. Now the tops of my legs rubbed together when I walked and they were often sore, and also my jeans didn't fit any more.

Claire came over looking great as she had lost a lot of weight, and after we ate some crumpets she made herself sick. I thought that maybe if I ate the food then was sick I could lose weight she had, so I made myself sick, but it didn't make any difference.

But I was on a high and was drinking heavily with friends, mostly alcohol we stole rather than bought from the local shop because the shop owner had seen us in our school uniforms. It got so bad that at one stage we even went to school intoxicated. We experimented with glue-sniffing, solvent abuse and dope, and we all smoked heavily. I would pack my mouth with toothpaste and chewing gum before going home.

I often got into fights and caused trouble. The gang of people I was involved with wore Nazi symbols on their coats and drew them on walls. I didn't quite know what this represented, but when they talked about the Anti-Christ, this worried me and it didn't seem right.

A lot of the older boys went through a phase of being tattooed and having their bodies pierced. We made cuts on our bodies and pushed the blood together to represent blood brothers and sisters. I pierced my ears many times and the pain of pushing an earring through my ear didn't hurt that much.

My dad complained constantly about what a mess I looked, but obviously I didn't think this at the time and I wanted to shock, rebel against society - I even had sex with one of the punks on a gravestone. I hated all religion! My friend, who was only 12 years old at the time, was with another of the gang carrying out the same sexual acts, but I had no respect for these guys or myself.

Chapter 2

I lost all respect for my dad. He said that my bedroom was a pigsty and that I would never make anything of myself, I was so untidy and he would not set foot in my house when I was older because it wouldn't be fit to live in. He moaned at me again for my hair being a mess, so I went to the barber's and had most of it shaved off, dyeing the small amount of hair I had left peroxide blonde. Some other girls did the same and we hung about with punks and skinheads and got into a lot of trouble. We would get into cars with them knowing that they had stolen the cars - we just didn't care. The aimless vandalism and destruction of property was releasing the frustration and hate I felt inside. I don't think Mum and Dad knew the half of it.

Dad did catch me in the local hang-out one night and told me off. His constant nagging really got to me and I went from one boyfriend to another, treating them all badly to prove that I was in control. If they showed signs that they were getting serious, or showed compassion or love, I would go off them very quickly. Everyone knew my dad and feared him.

The final straw came when my dad went into my bedroom and read all my letters from my friend William in Germany. In the letters, William often told me how he felt about me, but I didn't feel he was a threat and my feelings for him were very strong and I loved him, but only as a big brother figure. When my dad forced me to write to William and tell him that he was a loser and that I didn't want anything more to do with him, I was hurt and furious.

I had had enough! I even hid a knife under my mattress one evening but I knew this was not the way - I did have a conscience after all. I dreamed of walking into my parents' bedroom and killing him. I think that this had a lot to do with the pornographic and horror films which we had been watching when we should have been at school.

Living Behind the Mask

I knew what a light sleeper my Dad was and, although I could sneak out of the house, he probably would hear me, so I opened my bedroom window and stood on the window sill. I was wearing my bleached jeans, Union Jack braces, a white T-shirt, Doc Marten boots, and I got ready to jump. It was so far down. I asked myself, what would happen if I fell and broke my ankle? I wouldn't get very far and I needed to escape.

I decided not to jump and plucked up the courage to sneak downstairs, tip-toeing to avoid making the stairs creak. When I reached the back door I ran and ran as fast as I could to a friend's house where I chucked stones at her window to wake her up. We stayed out all night, stole some milk from a doorstep, then went to my boyfriend's house, but he didn't want to know. He wasn't worth it anyway.

We went over to the square where children met before school. I was 14 years old now, and when we met another skinhead girl who was younger than me and pregnant, we thought this was a grown up thing and we admired her. After everyone went off to school, I persuaded another of our friends, Sharon, to come into town with me and steal from shops. We often did this and even had orders from school friends for items of clothing.

We went on a stealing spree, graffitied some of the bus seats, then went into the Salvation Army where they gave us a cup of tea. We stole some sweets and chocolate bars from the tuck shop, then went into town and went from one shop to another. We had bags full of clothes, make-up, and toys, but when we went into another shop to get some pens to do more graffiti, Sharon was caught. I couldn't leave her, and I told the lady I was with her.

Chapter 2

The police were called and, although we gave false names, one of the policemen recognised me from the photographs my parents had given them earlier when they had reported me as a missing person. We were taken to the police station, locked up in separate cells and our belongings taken away, including our shoelaces in case we tried to harm ourselves. Luckily you don't get a criminal record if you are under 16.

To my surprise, my dad came alone and didn't shout, just held onto me. I froze and didn't want him to touch me, but he was supportive and really nice - he was just relieved to see me.

Who was this man? I hadn't seen this side of him before and it scared me. However, things hadn't really changed and after this he became more strict and clamped down on me even further. I began to starve myself.

I went to stay with my aunt and uncle who treated me really well and let me do what I wanted. My uncle even took me to the pub, and although I was too young to drink, I looked a lot older than I was. I didn't want to go home because here there wasn't any discipline and I loved it. I could be my own adult self, and although I did make a lot of mistakes along the way, it was fun.

My parents bought their own house. I got a regular boyfriend, James, who was domineering but I liked this - he wasn't a walk-over like many of my other boyfriends, and also my parents accepted him for who he was. Although I lost a lot of weight - my weight had dropped to eight stone - when I looked in the mirror I could only see fat, and I wanted to lose more. I took my exams at this time and got unusually high marks, especially in home economics and religious education, and

I wonder how much better could I have done if I had studied.

I started work with Mum in a nursing home as a junior auxiliary nurse. It wasn't very nice work, cleaning up after elderly people, and not suitable work for someone just out of school. There were three of us on trial, but it didn't work out, though I enjoyed helping the cook prepare the meals, and would stay over to watch her prepare the meals.

I didn't want to eat the meals, but loved to make meals for other people.

I wanted to join the Army, but my Father said it wasn't a life for a woman, adding that all the women were lesbians and that I was too small, anyhow. I hadn't grown since I was 12 and was still only 5 ft tall!

James started to hit me and beat me up. He got so possessive of me and jealous of other people, so scared of losing me that he would talk a lot about us getting married. He placed me on a pedestal as someone to be admired, but I didn't like this because when I looked at myself I only saw ugliness and I couldn't handle it. I finished with him and enjoyed watching him break down - I was in control now that he was crying like a baby.

I became very depressed and so useless that I couldn't see the point in living. I was alone on bonfire night because Dad had taken Joseph out and Mum was working. This was it, no-one around, so I might as well end it all. I hated myself, hated my dad, hated life. I put on some quiet music and took 100 aspirin tablets. The last handful was very difficult to swallow as they were so dry, even with a pint of water, the bitter powder taste lingering on my tongue. I felt myself go into a deep sleep. The next thing I knew I was in a hospital bed with a tube down my throat. I had my stomach pumped then was transferred to a mental hospital. Was I mad? I resented the fact that I was still alive.

My parents came to visit me, their failure. I had even failed in trying to end my life. I was in hospital for a week and when I came out my Dad got me a puppy and a cat. This was lovely, and I admired my Dad for bending over backwards to build a relationship with me.

He even made me laugh for the first time since my early years. He was such a miser and always tried to do jobs himself to avoid paying anyone. On one occasion, when he was trying to fix an aerial on the roof, Mum was at work, I was in my bedroom listening to music, and Joseph was watching television. My father had gone onto the roof about half an hour earlier, and when I heard some banging, I turned down the music and heard Dad shouting at the top of his voice.

My brother and I went outside to find that Dad was stuck and lying glued to the apex of the roof, unable to move. When he saw us he shouted for me to look in the Yellow Pages and call for an aerial repair man to get him down.

The trembling in my father's voice was so funny that I couldn't stop laughing. Joseph saw the humorous side of this, too, and we were almost crying when we phoned the aerial companies, but unfortunately all the aerial people were busy. We went out and told Dad who, by this time, was dripping with perspiration as the sun was hot. He started to get angry and gritted his teeth and told us to call the fire brigade and when the rescue team came, they tittered as they brought down the red-faced man. Mum couldn't believe what an eventful day we had had.

I managed to get a job as an office junior - a start, and I enjoyed the work. I was the youngest in a group of girls in the office and all the men worked upstairs.

Some of the older men were harassing me, but I started going out with one of them who was eleven years older than me and who spent an absolute fortune on me. When he proposed to me, I lost all respect for him, then dropped him. He couldn't handle it.

I had two ex-boyfriends pestering me now. If one wasn't phoning it would be the other one. The nice image of my dad disappeared and he reverted to the father I knew. I went on many diets, including a liquid diet for months, but I even cut down on the drinks and would miss the meals they suggested. I had a real sense of control.

I had to start paying Mum housekeeping money which I begrudged because I bought my own diet foods so why should I pay her? I didn't have enough money anyway, and none of my friends had to pay their parents to live at home. They ought to be grateful that I was still living there. (How wrong can a person be?) My periods stopped and I thought that I might be pregnant, but over the months nothing happened, so I assumed that I wasn't.

I saw Sharon again. She had left home and was living with a friend, Karen, and Karen's mum. She suggested that I meet Karen and ask if I could stay there, so we went round to the house. It was a mess compared to how clean and tidy our house was, but I saw it as a way out. Karen and Sharon spoke to her mother and she agreed that I could go and live there.

I went home and told my parents I was leaving because I had had enough of my dad being so hard and strict on me. He came into my bedroom when I was stuffing my suitcase full of clothes and begged me to stay. He cried - and this was the first time that I had seen my father cry - but I had no sympathy. I was such a cold person by now. I left home.

My eating deteriorated and my weight dropped to six and a half stone. Sharon was told to leave the house, but I had become quite close to Karen who was a year younger than me. She looked up to me - her sister had died of leukaemia and she said that I reminded her of her sister. The mother was a nurse and, concerned about my frail body, she tried to persuade me to see a doctor, but this frightened me. I thought I was eating normally, drinking lots of black coffee and eating a Kit-Kat for lunch, stretching the eating of it out to last a whole lunchtime.

I would nibble the chocolate off the sides then suck the wafer in the middle until it dissolved in my mouth. Sometimes I would eat an apple at teatime or a bag of crisps, but I would suck each crisp until it melted away. Karen's mother suggested that I might be anorexic. I didn't quite know the meaning of this, but thought it was a slimming thing and, after all, if I was eating chocolate and crisps then I was definitely not slimming, so she had to be wrong.

I was smoking heavily and drinking each night, and my health got so bad that I couldn't concentrate on my work. I was often ill and eventually handed in my notice at work.

I was going regularly to night-clubs and pubs with friends, although I was still under age. I tried taking my life on two more occasions, and the second time, when I was half conscious on a hospital bed, I could hear a lot of voices around me, one of them saying "Silly girl", and the whole place was a blur. At this point, I felt my head go to sleep, then I seemed to fly into a corner of the room and looked down on myself on an operating table, I had suction pads all over my chest, and I watched through the dazzling light as they gave my body a shock to try to get my heart beating again. No response. My whole body jerked, "one, two, three". At this point, a peace came over my body and I felt free. Should I stay here?

The light was blinding and I wanted to float towards the light, but at the end of the light I could see an eerie darkness. My life seemed to be mirrored all around me, like big cinema screens, with loud voices talking of my history, then the leprechaun heads started coming out of the dark tunnel towards me! I had to get away! I knew it wasn't my time to die. What had I done? I had to come back! I shot back down into my body - I wasn't ready to die after all. I emerged into my body and felt solid again, no longer that floating airy person.

As I re-entered my body, I knew that there was a reason for me to stay alive and that although I didn't understand what had happened I didn't want to share my experience with anyone because it sounded so weird. The boys who had found me and brought me into hospital were at my hospital bed, looking shattered. For weeks after they brought me flowers and chocolates.

I seemed to upset boys and give them the wrong impression. I longed to be loved, but loathed it when anyone felt so strongly about me that they wanted to take over my life and look after me. I hated anyone getting too close, for fear of being hurt.

Karen's mum took me to the doctors and they diagnosed me as having Anorexia Nervosa and said that, having had a near-death suicide attempt, I needed to be protected from myself.

To my horror, my parents were at the surgery because Karen's mother had contacted them, and they were the last people I wanted to see. They were so unhappy and had tried to get me back while I was still under the age to leave home, but they had been told to give up because by the time it got to court I would be old enough to leave home anyway.

I began to feel homesick. I had been referred to the psychiatric unit at the hospital, but I didn't see there was a problem. The house began to annoy me with its untidiness and dirt, and eventually I couldn't bear it any longer and went home.

My parents had moved house. I started going out with James again and my life began to settle down. I got a job as an office clerk and really enjoyed the work. Although I had been forced to see a psychiatrist, they didn't know what I was going through, but Mum insisted on taking me to the hospital and demanded that they saw me. I detested the smell of the hospital and the face of the psychiatrist and knew that to get away from this I had to lie - people wanted me to eat, so I must eat.

When Mum piled my plate up with food, I would eat it then vomit the whole meal up again. This was so easy to do and I didn't even have to stick my fingers down my throat because I'd learned to regurgitate food as a matter of course. I remained at the weight I was by exercising in my bedroom for hours, trying not to make a noise, embarrassed if anyone heard me, ashamed if someone asked if I was exercising.

I heard voices in my head, one saying "eat", the other saying "don't eat", or "if you do eat you will get fat", or when the one said "eat", the other would say "okay, eat, but you can't keep it in your body for long".

My parents were happy to see me eat but were puzzled when I wasn't gaining weight. My father disowned my eating disorder label and would not accept that I had a problem, seeing it as his failure. I bluffed the psychiatrist by lying, and they discharged me. I had won - they hadn't seen through my deceit, or I thought that they hadn't.

When Mum entertained her church home group in the house, I would go upstairs and block off my ears. I hated the music, but I could see they had something different. They seemed free and there was happiness in their eyes, a happiness I thought I could never experience. Why were these weird people different? My brother had been taken out of secondary school because he was being bullied, and was placed in the Christian School, I teased him about this, and Mum introduced me to some of her Christian friends' daughters, who seemed nice, but not my type - they were too good for me.

I wanted my freedom. I was coming up for 17 and desperately wanted a car, so my dad loaned me the money and we went out to look for a car. He took me all over the place and eventually we found a lovely black Mini - black was my favourite colour and I wore a lot of black baggy clothing which, my mum hated. My father spent a lot of time teaching me to drive, in conjunction with the driving instructor's lessons, and I even started having lessons from one of the boys from the local hang-out - a boy whom I knew could drive really well - I had seen him stealing cars before.

At work, some male colleagues hassled me, and one of them asked me out. I told him I was already seeing someone, but he persisted and I eventually gave in. Why did I always get this type of attention? They were only after one thing! I had finished with James again and he was even more upset this time. He bought me many presents and phoned continually.

When I went out for a drink with this guy, Paul, he made me laugh. I took him back to my parents' house and it was the first night of all-night-television, so we sat up all night. I thought that my dad was away, so I was very surprised when he came downstairs and, although he hadn't met Paul before, he was most pleasant, especially as it was 3 am in the morning!

Paul seemed to understand me and listened to me, and I felt that we were right for each other - I could sense it immediately. He felt the same about me and I found myself explaining about my Anorexia Nervosa. He didn't show any signs of disgust or withdraw from me and was quite relaxed about it. Did he know what he was letting himself in for?

Chapter 3

CHAPTER THREE

You can't run forever!

This new boyfriend was different from James and very nice, and although he told me he had his own place, little did I know he had a fiancée, so it was their place! I found out soon after, though, when Paul said he had ended their relationship, moved out of their flat, and rented a room in a shared house. I liked his independence, his danger, and his freedom.

My dad discovered that Paul was engaged and had an argument with him, resulting in my father picking Paul up by the scruff of the neck and warning him not to hurt me or Paul would have him to deal with. I was surprised that this didn't put my boyfriend off and, on the contrary, it made him even more determined. As far as I was concerned, if my dad disliked him, I would try harder to stay with him. I stayed at Paul's place most weekends and, to my surprise, my parents didn't ban me from seeing him. I think they realised I was growing up.

Paul owned a couple of motorbikes, and it was really exciting to be on the back of them, feeling the wind in my face and the exhilaration of speed. It was wonderful and he made me feel very special. I learned more about this new man in my life, that his parents were divorced, and his mother had an affair and re-married then moved to Devon with her new husband. We waved Paul's father off to Spain to re-live his youth.. He was very bitter about the termination of his marriage.

James continued to phone and would knock on the door, turn up at work, or prevent me from going to work - he was desperate, but I was happy with this new person in my life and wanted to put the past behind me. I loved going round to Paul's, and felt a maturity in playing 'the caring partner'. I would spend hours making wonderful meals for him, but would restrain from eating them myself, and it was a pleasure seeing someone enjoying the food I had prepared.

My eating patterns were chaotic. I would either starve myself or cram loads of food into my stomach until it was near to bursting point then literally crawl up the stairs and make myself sick. It was so degrading, and I would feel faint afterwards and break into hot sweats. I needed to have sugar because my blood sugar level had dropped so low due to the vomiting and left me feeling shaky and tired.

I would clean up the toilet, make myself presentable, and clean my teeth, totally de-contaminating myself. My parents became more aware of my eating habits and my father would open the drains outside when I went to the loo to see if I had made myself sick. Once he charged upstairs after I had had three helpings of Mum's spaghetti bolognese and physically ran his hand around the toilet pan and shoved it in my face after I had denied making myself sick. He showed me the residue in the bowl. I was repulsed at myself but I still had the little voices in my head, and when they turned to a total hatred of my father I had to get away.

I had only been going out with Paul for a couple of months when he wanted to take me to Devon to see his mother and stepfather. They were Christians and I felt they disapproved of me, and I did win them over but, of course, no-one is good enough for a mother's son, and his mother only persevered with me to keep her son happy. Whilst we were there, they suggested that we go to see Paul's uncle who owned his own painting and maintenance firm. He offered Paul a job as an apprentice painter and decorator, so we looked at our options. Paul was against it at

Chapter 3

first, but I saw it as my escape and a chance to regain my independence. I loathed having to rely on my parents and they couldn't handle my erratic mood swings - I was like a Jekyll and Hyde character.

We returned to Colchester and talked a great deal about moving, weighing up the pro's and con's. Maybe if I got away my eating habits would sort themselves out. I was fed up with waking up in the middle of the night dreaming about food, obsessed with how much I weighed, jumping on and off the scales, and if I gained a pound I didn't want to go out to see anyone because I felt fat and ugly. My life revolved around my self-image, but the binge cycle was a trap.

Mum did a lot of cooking for the church, so there was always something cooking. She would leave these meals cooking all day in the slow cooker, and it was as if they were shouting at me, "Come and get me!". I would scoop spoonfuls of food from these pots and then deny that I had touched it when Mum confronted me. On many nights I would sneak around the kitchen when everyone was upstairs in bed, carefully eating things which wouldn't be noticed - cereals, bread from the freezer - then neatly fastening the bags up again, eating left-over meals in the fridge and hoarding food in my bedroom. I would even stoop to eating food from the waste bins that took my fancy!

I knew that if I flushed the toilet chain people would hear me, so I would cram the food down the plug holes, frequently blocking the pipes. Sometimes the rotten smell was disgusting, but still I continued to do it although it was very embarrassing.

No-one knew how severe my problem was, and if anyone approached the subject I would turn very nasty. Even though Mum and Dad were only being caring and wanted the best for me, I needed my eating disorder - it was my secret, my best friend, a best friend I hated and loved at the same time. I went to great lengths to hide my problem, and I would even take the rubbish out with me so that no-one would detect the food wrappers.

Paul proposed to me. I didn't need much persuading so we got engaged. Then Paul's ex-fiancée came round to his place and started throwing things at him because, although he had told me he had finished their relationship, he had only told her it was a cooling off period, and behind my back he had been sleeping with her. I felt hurt, but the prospect of getting away prevailed and I covered up the feelings of betrayal.

We agreed to cut our ties with Colchester and leave for Devon. At work we had a big leaving party and the managers proposed a toast to me and said what a splendid job I had done and that I would be welcome back anytime, etc.

Unfortunately, they didn't do the same for Paul and he hardly had a mention in the goodbye speeches, so he felt bitter - he had given four years of his life to this company and they had praised me highly although I had only worked there for six months.

The next hurdle was to break the news to my parents. They didn't take it well and said I was making a mistake, and that I couldn't take anything out of my bedroom or take my car as I hadn't passed my test and hadn't finished paying back to my father the money I had borrowed. One of Paul's motorbikes had been stolen, and he sold the other one to buy a car. He paid my dad the remainder of the money on the Mini with his bonus pay and promised faithfully that I would not drive the Mini. I did, though, following Paul's car all the way to

Devon, without a licence.

We stayed with Paul's uncle and aunt for a few weeks until we found a flat of our own - a one bedroom holiday flat in Torbay. Paul started work and came home after work covered in paint splashes. However, I hated the flat being untidy or unclean and would pester him about the mess he left about the place, especially if I had spent hours making it perfect. On the other hand, Paul insisted on his dinner being on the table when he walked through the door, and this became like a ritual, leaving me feeling like a robot.

I spent a lot of my day bingeing and vomiting. I would buy in cheap bulky foods, easy to be sick on, and the continual purging, taking laxatives, took its toll on my skin, my eyes were puffy, my glands were up, making my face look blotchy and rounded, and I was frequently ill with kidney infections. I had gained weight, which scared me. I was getting rid of all the food I ate, so why was I piling on the pounds? As my weight increased, my periods started again but were very irregular, so the doctor put me on the 'mini pill' to regularise them.

For the rest of the day I would drive around in my car searching for work. I was stopped a couple of times by the police, once for speeding when they told me to slow down; the other was because one of the light bulbs was out.

My heart was beating so fast that I thought it would pop out of my mouth - I must get my licence or I could jeopardise getting a licence at all. My fiancé had modified the car and I was so angry when they failed me on my driving test even before we had taken it out. I could have killed him, but eventually I did pass the test and felt such relief as well as a sense of achievement.

I found employment quite quickly in a financial advisor's office which turned out to be a pleasant place to work. It made sense to buy a house because we would be paying less for a mortgage than we were paying in rent, but I was only 17, so this would be illegal, but if everyone was willing to help, then I could apply for a mortgage. We filled out the application forms and I was asked to go for a medical, which brought attention to me from the other girls in the office, because when they looked at my application form they asked me questions about my Anorexia. One particularly large lady who was desperate to lose weight was usually happy and jolly, but she became serious and asked "How can you catch Anorexia?" Could I pass it on to her?

I was horrified to think she was asking me if she could have some of what I had, and told her I wouldn't wish it on my worst enemy. They were so ignorant of what I had experienced and still was experiencing, and they were also unaware that I was still suffering and that now the Anorexia had progressed to Bulimia.

Through a lot of contacts with solicitors and people in the insurance firms we knew, we managed to purchase a property. It was wonderful, our bedroom had sea views over Paignton beach and it was a glorious sight in the mornings. However, Paignton was either packed with elderly people in the winter or with holidaymakers in the summer, and sometimes it would take me half an hour to get to work, though we only lived a mile away.

We had new, used, donated, and second-hand furniture to fill the house, and it was lovely. I kept the house so spotlessly clean that it was uncomfortable - even the garden had to be uniform. The neighbours were mainly elderly people or older than Paul and myself, so I didn't feel as though I fitted in very well. Someone even asked me which house my parents had moved into!

This was such an insult, I did look a lot older than I was! I started to meet new people and go out to night-clubs, but Paul didn't care for these very much. I was drinking very heavily, but I was needing more and more to get to the happy state and to get drunk.

There was a man called Hank who worked with Paul, and he did like going out. Hank made me laugh. We would go out as a foursome, and one evening I was hiding with Hank behind some trolleys, giggling while we waited for our respective partners to walk by - we had run out of the night-club to tease them. However, they didn't come and neither of us had any money on us, but Hank was a very spur of the moment person, and never ceased to amaze me.

He flagged down a coach which had been driving by and we hitched a lift. It was 3 am in the morning, and it was like something out of a film. The coach was empty, but the coach driver was lost, so we told him we could take him to where he wanted to go. Then we saw a taxi in front of us with our partners in the back, kissing - we couldn't believe what we were seeing. We asked the coach driver to stop at the traffic lights and we both jumped out.

Hank tapped on the taxi window and I will never forget the looks on their faces as we got in the taxi with them and drove home.

Our friends slept downstairs, but I kicked Paul out onto the landing. I hated him. What was I doing? We made up days later when Paul made the excuse that he was drunk, and then he turned the conversation round to asking what I was doing with Hank. I think his conscience was trying to put the blame on me. Hank came round to the house quite a lot, and became more my friend than Paul's. I confided in him and he in me. It was a totally innocent relationship, though, and he made me feel valued.

I started to feel very ill, and every time I smoked a cigarette I would go green at the gills and want to throw up. This was an unusual feeling - not to want to be sick. What was wrong with me? I had a lot of time off work and the doctors carried out many tests. Because I was very weak and pale, they suspected I was anaemic or diabetic.

To my surprise, it wasn't anaemia - I was pregnant! My fiancé's reaction was "get rid of it!", but there was no way I could destroy this child. Besides, I was four and a half months pregnant, I was now 18, wasn't I mature enough to care for a child? What type of mother would I be? One thing Mum's church people had taught me, if nothing else, was that life is very precious and abortions are destructive. I told Paul that if he wasn't happy with this then he knew what he could do, and this didn't go down well with him.

I felt very protective of the little person growing inside of me, scared, but also excited. I telephoned my mum and my parents came down a week later to visit. The house was very cold because although it was a new house it hadn't been fitted with central heating, so my father said he would lend us the money to heat the house because it would be too cold in the winter for a newborn baby. We were also having difficulty with one of the cars, and my company car would need to be surrendered at some point.

I was free to do what I wanted and could eat what I wanted - I was feeding two now. In the back of my mind I kept thinking "but after I have given birth what will I be left with? I must eat healthily so

Chapter 3

that only the natural weight for the baby will be gained". I was not a blossoming pregnant woman, and was ill quite a lot, although I had lots of energy towards the end of the pregnancy.

I worked throughout - probably too much.

I was even, at seven and a half months pregnant, a steward for Tapau and Status Quo concerts, where it was very hot and I was on my feet the whole time. Extra large T-shirts covered my rather huge bump now. I couldn't bear to look at myself in the mirror. I hated looking at myself in the bath because my legs looked huge and my ankles were all swollen, and I couldn't bear for people to see me like this. I didn't attend ante-natal classes as I didn't feel them to be necessary, but also I didn't want to feel I was member of this fat brigade!

I had been to see my solicitor to arrange to put the house on the market and to find out how we would go about a separation. Paul and I had decided it was for the best that we split up - he didn't want the baby and I didn't want him. He started seeing his old girlfriend and this made me angry. I was the stupid one, still making his dinner, cleaning his clothes, and cleaning the house. Luckily, the house market was soaring and we would make a nice profit out of it.

Another bombshell - a drunk driver reversed into my parked car. A neighbour saw them do it and caught up with them, but unfortunately the passenger side of my car had been damaged. I couldn't drive any longer because of the size of my stomach, and now when we went out anywhere I had to clamber over the driver's seat into the passenger's side.

During the last part of my pregnancy I became passive, and a lot more receptive to this stranger I was living with, and we regained the passion we had for one another. Deep down, I loved him, and decided it was for the best that we stay together for the baby's sake. We decorated the nursery and the house was beginning to look more like a baby warehouse: there was the cot, the pram, the changing unit, clothes, nappies, toys - I didn't realise that babies came with so much baggage, but my baby would not want for anything.

Paul confessed that he was scared, saying that he was too young to take on the responsibility of being a father. He blamed me and said I must have done it on purpose and stopped taking my pill, but this was not the case. Obviously, it was all the vomiting I had been doing, and the pill didn't have a chance. We agreed that it takes two to create a pregnancy, and we would face the consequences together.

As for the doctors, they had said that it was unlikely that I would conceive because of the damage Anorexia does to one's body. I couldn't tell Paul that I had also been very ill with Bulimia!

The baby was due on Paul's 21st birthday, but I was overdue. We had a joint birthday party for Paul and his sister on the 24th June 1989. A big cake was made, and all the family congregated - even his father returned from Spain. I had a few glasses of wine with a massive curry, and I had an unusually big appetite - without the guilt.

In the middle of the night I started to have heavy contractions. My fiancé was fast asleep and, having drunk a little too much, would be unfit to drive, so I went downstairs and prepared my bag for the hospital. I tidied up the house, prepared Paul's meals for the week, then placed them in the freezer (in between the pains). I needed to be busy until I was ready to go.

Chapter 3

I crept upstairs and tried to tell Paul that it was time, but he didn't move. Could I wait another couple of hours? Maybe I should make my own way to the maternity hospital. Fortunately, he woke up at 7am - and we set off for the hospital.

With difficulty, I climbed over the driver's seat into the passenger seat, but we only got halfway down the road when the car broke down. I don't know about having a baby, but I nearly had kittens! Paul fiddled about under the bonnet and got the car going again. At the hospital we were taken to the delivery suite, but there were complications so Paul went for some lunch, having been told that it would be hours before the baby came. When he returned, the baby was half out - a baby boy! This was the first time I believed that miracles could happen, it was such a wonderful experience. The pain disappeared and out of it came love.

I bonded instantly with this little boy of mine, and when I looked over to Paul he was crying. It was such an emotional moment. I was a mother and I would take care of this child and would bring him up totally different to the way I was raised. I don't blame my parents, but I want to be there and bring this little chap up. We named him Joshua David, Joshua because it was an unusual name at the time, and David, after my father.

We had many visitors, showers of gifts and - most special of all - my parents came to stay in a nearby holiday village to see their grandson. I was so proud, and my dad was so proud of me that my feelings for my parents changed at this moment. The bond between my Mum and Joshua was also very strong.

My body was weary after the labour, but my mind was urging me to get back into an exercise routine. The doctors advised me to wait at least three months, and in the meantime just to hold my stomach in and do pelvic floor exercises. I was determined that once I was strong enough I would go on long walks. I breast-fed Joshua for the first couple of months and this was supposed to bring your figure back. I found that my weight dropped to eight stone within two months. I walked Joshua everywhere and, as Devon is a very hilly place, pushing a pushchair up and down was great for me.

I loved being with Joshua but bingeing had crept back into my life. I was at home most of the day as I could not afford to pay a childminder to enable me to go back to work, but I did land myself a job in a local chemist's warehouse. It was good, and I made new friends and started to go out to night-clubs and pubs after my shift. Joshua kept me up most of the night crying, and Paul did not like getting up, saying that he needed to go to work the next day, so I restricted my sleep, sleeping only when Joshua slept. I didn't think I was coping well, for although I was doing everything I could to pacify him, still he cried, and it was such a high pitched cry that it would chill through my bones. I took him to the doctor, but he found nothing wrong.

I was changing his nappy one day when I noticed a large lump in his groin. He was screaming and kicking his little egs and the lump was hard. I took him to the doctor again, and he said that Joshua had a hernia, and instructed me, when the lump came up, to press it back in and it would stop the pain. In the meantime, "give him plenty of Calpol".

Paul bought me a motorbike for my 19th birthday, and it felt good to have something of my own. We had recently had to get rid of our cat because it kept jumping into the cot where it was nice and warm and we figured that this was dangerous, especially if the baby was in there.

Chapter 3

There was a scare at the time about cot deaths and I was paranoid.

My mind was still playing tricks on me, and I dreamt I was dying of some incurable disease. What would happen to Joshua? My fiancé wasn't responsible enough to care for him like I cared for him and, besides, I didn't want to die, I knew that I must stop my awful eating habits, but I relied on them for my sanity. I needed a break, so I went to visit my parents in Colchester. They were so good, and I loved showing Joshua off to my old school friends. Mum and Dad were such a help, for the pressure of Joshua's illness was becoming too heavy, and it hurt me to see him crying so much. Mum said I was losing too much weight and asked if I was looking after myself. Of course I told her that I was.

I told them how I felt trapped and wanted to go back to work, but explained the situation: money was tight with one income and I wanted the best for Joshua. Dad said his hands were tied, and they couldn't help so long as we were so far away. They wanted to help, but I would have to move back to Colchester. My parents looked at houses for sale and found a repossessed house on a nearby council estate with three bedrooms, which was a bargain at the time for a house of this size. Houses in Devon were so much more expensive and I felt we would need to move eventually when Joshua was older.

My hormones were pushed down, turned over, mixed up, then shaken together - I didn't know whether I was coming or going. Dad was a saint and let me catch up with my sleep. He would get up in the middle of the night and feed Joshua with the milk I had expressed earlier. It was wonderful, and it made me realise how little Paul helped with Josh.

When I returned home, Paul asked me to marry him and I thought I might as well - he was my baby's dad, after all. I did love him, even though he had funny ways. I could also get what I wanted, when I wanted it. I bought what I wanted, said what I wanted, he worked hard, and we had a good sexual relationship - so why shouldn't I marry him? I didn't deserve any better.

There was a wonderful registrar's office called Oldway Mansions which had a large marble staircase with brass fitments. It was a venue fit for a queen's wedding. It was perfect. I didn't want to get married in a church because I thought it would be hypocritical; I wasn't a Christian and didn't want to believe there was a God. For this reason also I didn't have Joshua christened.

I appeared to be so happy on the outside "such a bubbly person", but inside I hurt so badly that it bled. I loved my child and never wanted him to experience the same hurts that I had.

On my hen night, a bunch of the girls took me for a Chinese meal, then we went on a pub crawl. Some of the girls wanted to give the night-clubs a miss, so the remainder of us carried on. The stag night was on the same evening, and we thought the men would be in a different part of Torbay, but we bumped into them. I asked them where Paul was and they said that they had mixed him a concoction of drinks in the first pub which he couldn't handle and that he had disappeared. I didn't quite believe them, but we went back to one of the girls' houses, played cards all night and watched a couple of videos. We got a taxi home at 7 am to find Paul spread out on the front lawn. Apparently he had come home because he felt ill and had passed out.

On the 18th September 1989, I put on a fairytale dress, and Mum and Dad came down for the wedding. We had many photographs taken on

Chapter 3

the way to the registrar's office and my dad said I looked lovely. He also said that, if I wanted, I had time to back out and no-one would be angry, and that if I had any doubts we could turn the car around and go home. But everyone had gone to so much trouble that I felt I had to go through with it.

The ceremony was nice, the flowers and everything were perfect, but what was I doing? Was I ready for a commitment to anyone? I wore a false plastic smile all day. We went on to the reception where I spent most of the night drowning my sorrows with my father-in-law. I ended up by making myself very ill and I didn't want to go back to the hotel, so we went home and my mum cleaned me up. I was sick everywhere. What had I done?

In the morning I went downstairs and apologised to my parents who said it was okay. My new husband wasn't too happy, but we made it up on our honeymoon. Joshua went back with my parents and I missed him terribly and wanted to go and collect him. Paul was annoyed at this.

The honeymoon ended and we collected the baby from Mum's then drove back home, I carried on working to keep my sanity, and a lady down the road baby-sat for Joshua until Paul came home from work, but often he would forget to collect Joshua, or would get home early and not pick him up. It was like having two babies. Paul would rage if his dinner wasn't on the table when he got home, or would remark if the house was the slightest bit untidy, but he would spend hours on his cars rather than spend time with Joshua and myself.
I was being hassled at work by some of the men and they kept asking me out. Why did this always happen? I tried to be nice to everyone, but men always took my kindness the wrong way. I wanted to go back

to daytime work because I was fed up with the disruption and I wasn't happy with Paul's neglect of Joshua. I phoned Mum to ask if I could visit them. They jumped at the chance and my father drove down to collect me.

My dad was different. He had "given his life to Christ", and was so nice and gentle that I could hardly believe it was the same person. Mum was due to go to Israel with her friend, but suddenly Joshua's hernia came up and wouldn't go back down. It was black, and he was holding his breath, Dad panicked and took me to the doctor's surgery with Joshua, where they quickly arranged for Joshua to be admitted to hospital for an emergency operation.

It was breaking my heart to hear him crying. He wanted some milk, but they said he was 'nil by mouth' and hung him upside down with his legs all bound and I couldn't sleep in the same room as him. I was there for every minute the hospital allowed and I was exhausted.

When Joshua came home, he was a changed boy, so placid and, compared to how he was before, it didn't seem as though he cried at all. My dad was a great strength and a wonderful man - not the man I once knew. I still abused my body with the food, especially whilst Dad was at work, for now he was no longer with the army and he was commuting and working in an office in Hertfordshire.

While Mum was in Israel, Dad and I discussed my moving back so that I could work in Colchester and Mum could look after Joshua. The house over the field from my parents was still for sale and it would be so convenient. I knew I had made another mistake. My marriage was only a couple of months old but I didn't want to go back to Devon. When Mum returned she persuaded me to go to church with them.

Chapter 3

I went along to church with my parents, and when I walked into the church hall it was crammed full with these happy-clappy Christians. The music started and I wanted to run out screaming. I couldn't speak and just sat there and wept. I had made such a mess of my life, and I felt jealousy towards these people because I could never have what they had. I was too bad, not good enough.

I phoned Paul and told him that I wanted to put the house on the market and that, as I no longer wanted to be with him, I was staying with my parents. I told him, too, that I had got a job in a local leasing company, and that Mum was going to look after Joshua while I went to work.

Paul hadn't take it all in when I had blurted all this out, so he drove up to Colchester the next day and begged me to stay with him, saying that he would kill himself if I left him. He said he would change and that he would help me more in the house. I felt sorry for him and agreed to go back with him and sort things out as my job didn't start for another month. Luckily, the house sold immediately.

My husband stayed in Devon while the house sale and the purchase of our new property was going through, and I started my new job. It was great, Mum looked after Joshua as her own, and the relationship between my parents and myself was stronger than it had ever been.

I was feeling unwell, so I went to the doctor, but my illness continued and I was very tired. I thought perhaps it was something to do with my working environment because the place was very smokey and when one of the other girls had complained they had had air vents fitted.

Joshua was ten months old now and a lovely little boy, and my parents loved him. Paul managed to get employment with a local painting and decorating firm. I went up to the yard a few times with Mum to collect the car, or to collect paint or whatever, and we met a few of the office workers. One man came and chatted to us. He was about Mum's age, and he said that we looked like sisters. We did look alike, but not that close in age! The managing director, Harold, also took an interest in me, and asked me loads of questions, like where did I work and who was my husband. Harold was inquisitive, but he seemed to be a nice man.

In the painting industry, when it rains during an external decorating job, obviously you can't work, but instead of collecting Joshua or spending time with his son, Paul would go home and have a bath, then watch television. I couldn't understand this because I felt that I didn't spend enough time with my son and seized any opportunity I could to be with him. Paul still expected me to wait on him, cook his meals, and clean the house - he was taking advantage of everyone.

We moved into our new home which needed a lot of time, energy and money to be spent on it. The neighbours seemed to be quite nice on first meeting, and they helped us to clear the house of all the old carpets and rubbish. It was a nightmare - the carpets were infested with fleas, my white socks turned black as we walked in, some kids had been playing and had spread paint all over the garden, a dog had been locked in the house for a couple of months, and it smelt foul.

We found used syringes, an empty shotgun holder and hundreds of pornographic magazines. It was horrible, but I could see beyond this that it had potential.

To top it off, the results came back from the doctor. I was pregnant!

Chapter 3

Again, my husband said to get rid of the baby or else! He said we couldn't afford it and I thought, "Hello, I've been down this road before". I told him it was me with two babies, or he could go, so he came round to the idea. Another Joshua would be wonderful. Joshua was looking more and more like Joseph as he got older.

The house took a long time to decorate and bring up to a liveable standard, and there was still an eerie feeling about the place. There was a chill under the loft hatch, but the roof was insulated and there was no draught. We heard cries in the middle of the night which was scary, and there were unexplained noises. Mum said she could sense evil spirits in the house, and although I thought this was a load of rubbish, I did have a horrible feeling about this place. The wallpaper on the children's bedrooms was awful, and we found the chopped-off ponytail of one of the girls who had lived there previously.

The neighbours were gossips and they told us some horrific stories about our house and what had gone on in it. We took what they said with a pinch of salt until a plumber, a man from Mum's church, came into the house and said that he could feel that children had been abused in the house and that there was an evil feeling in it. He offered to pray for the house, and anointed each door frame with oil. I don't know what he did, but the house went warm from then on. Could there be some truth in this God thing?

I got bigger in this pregnancy than I had been during my pregnancy with Joshua. This baby was due in the winter, and I felt fat and frumpy and still dissatisfied with my life, but I didn't let it show. My job didn't last long as I had to take maternity leave. Mum said that she couldn't cope with two babies and that, as my dad was finding commuting difficult, they had accepted the offer of a transfer to Hertfordshire. I felt hurt and abandoned.

I had moved back to be with them and now they were moving away, and, on top of this, the neighbours were showing their true colours. They were malicious gossips and I didn't fit in. They thought I was a snob.

On the16th January 1991, something began to happen. I got up and did all my ironing. The Gulf War had just begun and I watched it on television all night. The contractions became very painful, so I telephoned my mum and woke Paul. It was 6.30 am when we dropped Joshua off at Mum's house then drove on to the maternity hospital. Daniel Thomas was born at 10.30 am, and he was lovely, but totally different from Joshua. Paul didn't seem as interested this time, although Daniel looked exactly like him.

I went home at 6 pm that evening. How was I going to cope? I was expecting Daniel to be the same as Joshua, crying continually but, to my delight, he was a placid child. He was slightly heavier than Joshua had been and ate a lot more, but that was all he seemed to want. Joshua was now toddling about and talking, but was jealous of his new brother.

A few months later, Mum and Dad moved to Hertfordshire. I had to buy loads of baby things again because I had sold most of Joshua's first baby things, thinking I wasn't going to have any more children. Paul accused me of Joshua's not being his, and he blamed Hank, saying "How can two boys look so different but come from the same parents?" I was insulted. I had not slept with anyone else since we had been together.

One evening, Joshua woke up and said that he could see the image of a man, then went on to described my Granddad King perfectly. He even told me that it was Granddad King and that he was showing such love and comfort to Joshua.

Joshua had never seen photographs of my grandfather and hadn't even heard me speaking of him, so to me this was another confirmation that there was a spiritual world.

My husband was spending more and more time on his stupid cars, and I begrudged this time. It occurred to me that this obsession with cars was really quite like an eating disorder:

"Imagine you are a Wolsey, baby blue in colour, born in 1958, and a bit plain. It is morning and you have been outside all night, your windscreen and windows are all frosted up from the cold autumn night, your engine is cold. Your passenger door lock is being fiddled with, it has frozen and a little anti-freeze is sprayed in and your joints start to moan as the door opens. Your owner hops across the passenger seat - your driver's door hasn't worked for years, it packed up when you had a collision with another car, it could have been repaired, but that scar is with you for life, but you can now live with it.

In order to get you started, you need some loving care, some motivation to get going. If only a warm blanket had been laid over your ice cold engine, maybe you would want to start. Instead, the key is turned in the ignition and you groan and splutter. What is the point of turning the cogs, whirring your wheels? Someone wants you to, and if you don't start, this person's day will be ruined and they will be angry with you.

Here we go, no anti-freeze to maintain the radiator, just a top up would keep you going. The engine ticks over for about five minutes, the windows are steaming up inside, the driver gets out and scrapes with windows clean, big puffs of smoke chugs out of the exhaust pipe, the service is long overdue, out it pours - all the pollution into the air. You don't mean to hurt anyone, it just seems to harm people who are around.

You must not feel guilty about this, circumstances have caused this. Time to go, in jumps your owner, clambering over the seats once more, he catches his buckle on your torn seats, the tearing of neglect when you were a young vehicle.

You have been going all day, your fuel has burned up. You drive into the local petrol station, the trickle of the petrol into your tank relieving the straining on your engine, slowly it filters through your engine and you are really hot, concentration is now good, you're raring to go. Your driver is a long way from home. He presses down on your throttle hard, you are at full speed all the way home, it is getting dark, on go your lights, it starts to rain, the windscreen wipers are on fast, you can cope, you convince yourself! It is getting colder, the heater is on, the radio is blaring out as company for your driver, you are getting very weary, your lights dim and your radiator shuts down.

Your almost bald tyres crawl into the drive, trying to grip onto the slippery path, longing to go into the big garage with the other cars, it seems so out of reach, the Mercedes gets regular unleaded petrol and can handle it, regular services and runs smoothly, if only you could operate like that. The next morning, once again you are frozen all over. Your insides are gurgling, hungry for oil, your dipstick is clean, still the driver needs to get to work, he goes through his routine of starting your engine, warming up your cold body, scraping the windows, you need an extra push this morning to get you going. You are irritable and jumpy, you feel weak and dizzy. You decide that you can't carry on any longer, you need oil to keep you going, you have no sense of control, you are desperate. You stop! There is a blackout.

As you come round, your driver is pouring in the fresh oil, you have a taste and taste some more, you nudge him with your bumper, desperate to fill your tank, you've had too much, it spills over the sides, your engine will find this hard to burn up, so you empty it through a crack in one of your pipes, you aren't used to running on this much energy, get rid of it!

You spark up again, your owner drives you into a brand new garage, they give you a complete overhaul, they repair your dent, repair your seats, change your gearbox, give you a complete service, wash, wax and polish, you are gleaming like new.

You drive out of the garage a new car, you have a new person to greet you, there is hope for anyone, but you must be treated right, nurtured, there may be hiccups along the way, but you are on the right track to being put right.

The old memories are there but they can be worked on, these experiences can be avoided by learning about yourself, continual maintenance is essential. This will keep the AA men away.

Liken your body to the body of the car: there may have been hurts along the way, but people with eating disorders use food as a comfort and release - it's their way of coping with a difficult world. We need food for energy to survive, like the car needs petrol and oil to keep going. We should allow ourselves selfish time, to be pampered once in a while and relax. If you don't, your body will burn out, so allow yourself this time. Don't feel that you have to please everyone around you. No-one is perfect and no-one is superhuman.

You can enter that big shiny garage by asking for help. You can be maintained, but you need to cry out and ask for it. You haven't got clocks and gauges to tell people what you are thinking, and people can't read your mind.

You can't recover from an eating disorder in a lonely world, so if you can't ask for help from a human, speak to the Lord Jesus Christ, He is the best listener you can have and He can help.

CHAPTER FOUR

Out of Destruction can develop Creation

Daniel hadn't long been born when I felt that I needed to return to work, I needed to meet people and to get away from the schizophrenic neighbours. One minute I was their best friend and the next they hated everything to do with me. I couldn't cope with such an uneasy atmosphere.

I went to my old company's function and, as usual, Paul didn't want to come - he hadn't been invited anyway. Everyone there asked me if I was going back to work in the office, but I explained that I couldn't because my parents had moved away. I had lost a lot of weight after having Daniel, so it was a mistake to drink the same amount of alcohol as I would have before. I fainted and had an epileptic fit, which was scary - I had never experienced anything like this before. My friends gave me a lift home.

I went back to work for a few evenings and at weekends in a local shop where I met new people and made friends with some of the girls at the shop.

Paul's workplace was changing, and some of the office people had left to set up another company. Harold came round to the house and offered Paul a job in this new company, but Paul said that he was settled where he was and didn't want to change jobs. I could see that he didn't have anything to lose by changing to the new company and, if most of the office workers had left, what was going to happen to the company he was currently working for? I managed to persuade him to move over.

Living Behind the Mask

On the first week of the new company's opening, the secretary fell ill and would be off for at least a month, so Harold asked me if I would fill in until she came back and I agreed. I met two of the directors whom I hadn't seen before, one of whom thought he was Mr Wonderful.

He was the youngest director and at 27 was proud of having reached the position of company director - quite an achievement for someone so young, although I saw him as quite old.

I was 20 years old at this time!

Everyone was pleasant and the work was interesting. Harold took me out to lunch on most days and bought me presents and, although this did seem unusual, I didn't see anything wrong with it as long as I was honest with Paul - and he didn't mind what I did.

The month ended and I went back to part-time work. In the meantime, I had built up a close friendship with my old school friend Sharon who had two daughters now and who was quite happy to earn money when I needed someone to look after my boys while I worked.

On most weekends Sharon and I would go out after I had finished work and spent most of our days together. We would go to the beach, sunbathe in the back garden, go to town, to the park - we even went to the fair without the children. We got on really well and when she confided in me about the horrible childhood she had had and how she had been abused, leaving her with a problem with her self worth, I realised I was not alone in feeling rejected.

I looked in the Yellow Pages for a helpline on Eating Disorders, but

Chapter 4

there wasn't one. I called the Citizens' Advice Bureau, and I was afraid that someone would recognise my voice. I don't know why I thought this because I didn't know anyone in the Citizens Advice Bureau. They gave me a telephone number in Norwich, and it took me a long time to pluck up the courage to speak to someone, but eventually I made the call and asked them if there was some sort of help group in Colchester. They said that there wasn't, but that they could send me some information. It was useless. I was alone.

Paul didn't really like Sharon. We suspected Paul of seeing someone else, but I didn't care - my respect for him had gone long ago. It might be a way out for me and, after all, he didn't want to spend any time with me or with the boys. My marriage was falling apart and I knew something had to be done about it.

I told Paul that I wasn't happy with the way he treated me but if he were to be more helpful then maybe I could regain respect for him. I had developed a lot of friendships but most of them didn't really involve him. I even had friendships with men, but nothing sexual, I just wanted to be noticed by Paul. I had many people asking me out but I remained faithful to him.

If we did go out together to pubs and discos, I would go off with my friends and ignore him. Even at Paul's company functions I would end up dancing with other people. We had to face it - we were drifting apart. I was drinking very heavily and starving myself for half of the day, then bingeing and vomiting in the other half. When I had settled the children down, I would exercise frantically, usually in the early morning and at tea-time.

My life was a shambles. The only things I cherished in my life were my two boys! I wanted to make something of my life, so I started various college courses, which were tough, but I felt I was directing my time into something positive and it might help to stop the binge cycle.

I had some very embarrassing moments with my binges. Once when the toilet was full of regurgitated food, as I flushed the cistern the whole of the toilet filled up with water and the sick floated to the surface. It was disgusting, and I thought it might overflow, with sick spilling over the side and seeping under the floorboards and through the kitchen ceiling - everywhere would be contaminated!

I had to go downstairs and confess to Paul that I had been sick. I told him that I wasn't feeling very well and that the toilet had blocked. He did un-block it, but he realised that I hadn't been poorly and that I had lied. A few weeks later Paul and a couple of his mates were laying a new patio in our garden, and he had to lift the manhole cover. To my horror, the drains were blocked and he had to get some rods and clear the drains of the residue of vomit up the sides. The smell was revolting.

After this, I made sure that I cleaned the drains thoroughly, and I had clean pipes from then on. They were de-polluted with bleach regularly as I didn't want to face the shame of calling a drain cleaner out and having to explain the blockage, especially as we knew our plumber personally.

I continued to do temporary work with Paul's company, but the young director, John, was beginning to annoy me with his remarks which were full of innuendoes. I thought he was a sleaze because he was married with two children. When he came round to the house one lunchtime, I didn't see it coming when he asked me out for a drink. I was too polite to tell him to 'stick it', but when I told him it wasn't right

Chapter 4

because we were both married, he responded casually with "Well, if you don't ask, you don't get". Such a slime ball!

I was insulted to think that he thought I was available and that I would be attracted to him. He was not at all my type, and when I next went to work at the office I tried to avoid him. Harold was paying me a lot of attention and he was nice, but little did I know that this would all turn sour. On a couple of occasions when John gave me a lift to the bank he would say things like "You will give in one day, I'm never wrong, I know you want me". I didn't!

A year and a half later, I started full time with the company. The first year had been very successful and they built me an office of my own and we hired a Youth Training girl. Harold sent me gifts, and would call me up on the telephone and ask me to spy on other members of staff, but he was passing personal credits through the accounting system and asked me not to say anything to anyone.

He took me on training courses with him and also took me down to meet everyone at head office. He had a way of making a person feel special. The crunch came when he started harassing me, making sexual remarks and suggesting that if I left Paul, he, Harold, could show me what life was all about and that I could have a much better life with him. I was disgusted - he was so old, in his fifties, fat and balding, yet, and I couldn't understand it, his girlfriend was the same age as me.

Harold was jealous when I went out at weekends, and would tell me that I could do better than Paul, but I had some values. I had married Paul for better or worse and I vowed that this would be my only marriage. John continued to pester me, but at least he was nearer to my age and I had started to see a different side to him. He was always smartly dressed and I began to understand him a bit more.

On his birthday, he asked me for a birthday kiss. I refused it, but a few months later when we went to a party he followed me upstairs to the toilet and, as I came out, he grabbed me and dragged me into the bedroom where he kissed me and touched me. The place was dark and when I came to my senses and realised what was happening, to my surprise, I was enjoying it.

We went outside and I told him that I liked the way he kissed - I had drunk a little too much. When he phoned me the next day and asked me out again, I said that I had been drunk the previous evening and hadn't known what I was doing. I felt guilty - what we had done was wrong … but something inside of me was stimulated.

The harassment from Harold got worse so I had to tell someone. Paul said that it was just his way and that I was just to ignore it. I confided all my concerns about Harold to John, who understood, but he asked me to reveal to him the receipts that were being put through the company books. I was uncomfortable about this, but I agreed to go to the office on the weekends to show John the receipts. I felt that I was betraying Harold but, after all, what he was doing was illegal.

I was beginning to feel attracted to John. I wasn't getting any younger and Paul showed me little attention - he was always too tired. John paid me compliments and appreciated me, and I found it very difficult to accept that someone would find me attractive because when I looked at myself I felt repulsed.

John telephoned me at home and asked me to go round to his house. I amazed myself by agreeing because I was lonely and wanted some attention.

I told Paul that I was going to college, which I usually did on a Wednesday evening but, of course, I went to John's house where we talked and kissed and cuddled. I think John wanted more but I didn't want that.

I was on a high the next day. John would steal a kiss in the office and I couldn't wait for us to meet again. We met in various locations after that, driving to different pubs and restaurants and calling each other continuously. We were falling in love without realising it.

I had the utmost respect for John who was kind, gentle, and firm but loving. We even risked a meeting in the park with the children to go out for a walk together. John would arrange extra work for Paul at the weekends and John's wife worked every weekend. Sometimes we met in McDonalds and sneaked a quick kiss here and there. The children got on really well.

We would go to hotels and stay overnight, and managed to get the money together without our respective partners knowing by saying we were on a training course, or made some silly excuse. Paul did start suspecting something, and work colleagues were also questioning the relationship between John and I because our personal phone calls were showing up on our mobile phone statements.

At birthdays and Christmas we bought each other presents and would have to lie about who bought them. We put notes in each other's desk drawers, and John frequently left a chocolate bar on my seat for when I came into work. He said that he couldn't buy me lots of presents, but I didn't mind, it was he who brought me happiness, not gifts, and I realised at this point that you can't buy people.

We went on holiday with our respective families although it was hard for us to be apart; John called me from France and I called him when I went to Greece. We had told our very close friends about our affair, although this probably wasn't the wisest decision to make.

When John said he wanted to spend the rest of his life with me, I had to be honest with him and confess that I was suffering from an eating disorder, to give him a chance to back out before we went any further, but he didn't, and insisted that he wanted to help me. I had seen a poster in the local doctor's surgery which gave a helpline number for people suffering from eating disorders, and I started to attend self-help groups on a Wednesday evening. I wasn't really ready for this, but it opened my eyes to the fact that I wasn't the only one suffering. However, the support provided by the Wednesday evening group wasn't enough and I soon stopped attending.

Neither John nor I could bear the thought of losing our children and we couldn't work out how to tell our partners our marriages were finished. John and his wife had grown so far apart that they were like strangers living in the same house. I couldn't bear Paul to touch me and when he walked in the room I cringed, feeling that I was betraying John.

John was jealous if I went out with my friends and he didn't like it when Harold made suggestions or bought me presents. He made ground rules and said that when we eventually got together I wasn't to go out to night clubs by myself. He said it wasn't natural for me to have male friends outside of the relationship, especially because of the way in which the two of us had been tempted. In retrospect, this seems fuzzy now and so far away.

A girl in the office told us that she visited a Clairvoyant frequently and that this woman was very precise. I was terrified and reluctant to see this woman, but John was intrigued, so we made an appointment. When we went to see her, the room we were shown into it was very hot because the fire was lit. It was devoid of ornaments. I took off my coat and sat on a pink leather suite.

The lady was a huge black woman who looked like Whoopey Goldberg. She said that she worked with two spirits, one being "Silver Wings", and that she would jump from past, present and future. As she spoke, the room went freezing cold although the fire was still blazing. The feeling in the room drained both John and myself, but I took notes of everything she said. It was so exact that it was scary and John and I came out empty, feeling that there were definitely evil spirits in this room.

There was still the problem at work with Harold. We had enough information on him to get him out of the company as what he was doing was illegal and he was encouraging others to assist in his fraud. A board meeting was called where John presented all the information to the chairman and although everyone gave their views, the chairman said that there wasn't enough evidence against Harold, which was totally wrong. John was accused of being a revolutionist and of having persuaded other members of staff to jump on the bandwagon, which wasn't the case.

On the same day, one of the other directors was acting very strangely and we thought he was experiencing a breakdown but, after vigorous tests, it transpired that he had a brain tumour. Harold apologised to me and said he didn't mean to cause any offence, so he was let off, but the atmosphere in the workplace was awful and very hostile.

John and I continued to see each other in secret and we would go to parties and steal the odd kiss. When Paul suspected something was going on, he kicked John's car and caused a lot of damage. John's wife also suspected something was going on because she had found a receipt for lingerie, but John lied as to where it had come from and got away with it temporarily.

Our future was soon taken out of our hands. Late one evening, I was in the bath when Paul decided to look in my briefcase and he discovered a love note from John. He charged into the bathroom and threw it into the water. Stunned, I watched the ink filtering to the top of the bath tub. I didn't know what to do.

Paul hurled abuse at me and told me to telephone John and tell him to come round to the house. I told him that I couldn't do that in case John's wife answered the telephone, but he gave me no option. I had to call John. It was 11.30pm and, to my relief, John picked up the receiver, and I told him he had to come round now or my husband would go and see him at his home.

John showed up and told Paul of his intentions and that he wanted to be with me and that I wanted to be with him, and that he would care for Joshua and Daniel. Paul was not happy, to say the least, and he told John to go home and tell his wife or he would call her.

After John left, Paul threw me out of the house. I had no coat and it was very cold as I walked down the road to my friend's house. I had no loose change so couldn't even call anyone. In the meantime, Paul had smashed the house up and had called a friend to come over before he did something he would regret, and his friend saw me walking down the road and gave me a lift back. After a long talk, he calmed my husband down, but I didn't get any sleep that night, as you can imagine.

I took the children to school and tried not to let them know what had gone on. I don't know what I was thinking at this point. Would John back out? Even if he did, I decided I didn't want to carry on life with Paul. The following day John and I met Harold for breakfast and told him everything and he wasn't surprised. John hadn't told his wife, Paul had done that for him, and she had phoned the office and given me a piece of her mind, which was justified.

I telephoned my parent's house hoping to talk to my mother, but she wasn't there. My dad answered the phone and I told him everything. I remember starting the conversation with "Dad, you won't believe what I have done this time", then I cried and poured my heart out. He was so understanding, I couldn't believe it, he was so positive and supportive.

Earlier on in the year my parents had separated and he had been to stay with us for a while, so he understood how much I needed him now.

John's wife came in and chucked all of John's dirty linen all over the office. There were smelly socks and dirty clothes over the chairs and desk in John's office, which was embarrassing for John.

Paul came in for paint a few times and suggested that we could try again - put it all behind us - but it was too late, I didn't want him, so he moved out of the house, saying goodbye to the boys but promising that he would continue to see them.

I was agreed that it would be best if I left the company. I got a job immediately working for the managing director of a treasury company where the pay was excellent, the people seemed genuine, and the office environment was so different from what I was used to. John and I met most lunch times.

John told his daughters that he wouldn't leave them, but that he didn't love their mum any more so he was moving out of the house and into his parents' house.

Miraculously, Paul acquired a girlfriend immediately and they soon moved into a house together. Paul usually turned up late on his day to have the boys, or didn't appear at all, and this was heartbreaking for the children. He had agreed to pay maintenance but didn't pay a penny, and then the Child Support Agency got involved.

By this time, John had moved into the house with me and we had his girls, Lauren and Ellis, on a regular basis. All the children settled in really well together. Sadly, our old work colleague passed away and it was very uncomfortable at the funeral amongst old friends and work friends. Harold was there, but most of our friends had abandoned us and had taken the sides of our ex-partners, which isolated us socially as a couple, but it allowed us time to adjust to our new relationship.

I was insecure and felt inferior to others. I found myself clamming up or waffling on about anything to cover up my feeling of inadequacy.

My communication seemed to have broken down and I would have to force myself to telephone my family and friends - I didn't have many left! I found myself writing lists of what needed to be said so that I wouldn't be in the embarrassing situation of drying up in conversation and having them talking about me behind my back, saying what an idiot I was.

Chapter 4

John left the company and set up his own painting and decorating company. Our families accepted what had happened, and when John and I went to visit my parents with the children one Sunday, Mum said that it would be nice if the children went to Sunday school with her, but that she couldn't cope with four of them by herself. I dreaded this moment but, to my surprise, John agreed to go. Unfortunately, Ellis, John's youngest daughter, didn't like him to leave her, so he had to go to Sunday school with her, and I was left to go with my mother to the main service. I found myself unexpectedly enjoying the service. It wasn't boring, it wasn't irrelevant, it was interesting, and the music was good. There was a baptism during the service, which fascinated me, and I felt a great sense of peace.

My eating was even more chaotic than ever and I couldn't understand it. I did want to get better. I craved normality but didn't know how to go about it. My mother said that God could heal me if I allowed Him to. I was fed up with people saying to me "How do you stay so slim?". I felt like replying, "Because I throw up after I eat everything", but, of course, I would not admit this to anyone - the disease is so secretive and I was living in a different, inner world. It is like being taken over by the cravings, not caring what food you eat, and even eating food which is half cooked or even half frozen, knowing the dangers of this but not caring.

Throughout the week I couldn't stop thinking about the church, and I knew the children had enjoyed it, too. I knew Mum had been involved with an evangelical church in Colchester, but it wasn't in the same building that I had gone to years previously. I telephoned the Christian school who put me in touch with the new church leader, and the following Sunday I took the children along. John felt uneasy about going with us, so he stayed at home.

I walked in to be greeted by two ladies, Julia and Melissa, who made me feel very welcome. They hugged me and sat with me, and they remembered my mother and were encouraged to see me.

One of the ladies explained how she had prayed for me when I was in my teenage years and that they had prayed for my salvation, so it was like a miracle for them to see me there.

I didn't feel in the least bit uncomfortable as the church was so alive. There was a worship band at the front and they were singing an old Beatles hit, with slight alterations - "Then I saw his face, now I'm a believer, etc.". It was excellent.

They moved all the congregational chairs from the floor and we danced. I felt a freedom, and as I looked into the eyes of these people, I saw the sparkle of happiness in their lives, but I was too scared to take this step of faith myself. Did I want this Jesus? I wanted the happiness, but I didn't think I could handle the commitment.

When I went home I told John how brilliant the service had been. I couldn't stop talking to him about it all week, so when he said on the following Saturday evening that he wanted to come along with me I was shocked because throughout the week he had been rejecting my suggestion that we go to church again on Sunday.

This was in November 1995 and we had been living together for seven months now. As we walked into the church, we had the same warm homely greeting that I had received the week before. John kept making sighing noises when the people were praying and I thought he must be

Chapter 4

bored or thinking that I had finally flipped. I wasn't very secure in my life or our relationship. I couldn't come to terms with the fact we were together and that John wanted to be with me, it was too good to be true.

It seemed very relevant to us when two people gave their testimonies, talking about how they had recently come through to the Lord through an Alpha course, which is a basic introduction to Christianity.

The church was launching one of these courses in the new year to run over a number of weeks, to consider Who is Jesus? How to Pray, the Holy Spirit, and the Bible - as it says, a basic course. It sounded wonderful but my neck prickled when they said that there was food at each Alpha night. This terrified me, but the draw to this course over-rode the feeling.

To my surprise, I was totally wrong about John's reaction because he loved the service and had got chatting to a man called Craig in the church who talked to John about football, and suggested that we go to the evening session. I was on a high, thinking, "These people aren't weird, they are normal people but they have something I haven't - Jesus".

We managed to get a baby-sitter so we were able to go to the evening service. John said that he had found what he was looking for in life and when they invited people to go and be prayed for, John went up.

He was desperate to feel what these Christians were experiencing. Julia said that she saw a lot of bitterness in John's heart and that maybe we should both go up and pray for him. Me pray for him? I couldn't do that because I didn't know how to pray and I would be very embarrassed about doing so, and anyway I was not worthy. It was okay for John to go for prayer, but I was quite happy to sit in the back row and watch.

I was nudged forward, however, and although I felt uneasy, I knew this bitterness inside John was towards Harold and towards Paul. Julia told me to tell John but I couldn't - I was so insecure and afraid, so I asked her to do it. Julia got up and told John that if he didn't release his bitterness towards a situation or person, he wouldn't feel God's presence. He went up again for prayer - he was persistent.

Julia grabbed my hand and said that the two of us would just to stand with John to provide moral support for him, which we did, and then one of the leaders came to pray for me. I felt cool air breezing around me and I went all cold, then hot, and then it was as though I was fainting or falling asleep on the spot.

I felt great pains in my stomach and experienced almost a feeling of wanting to vomit. I knew at this point that God wanted to heal me of my eating disorder. The Lord filled my whole body with peace and there was a re-birth in me.

Julia explained that the Holy Spirit was working inside me, and it was a feeling I had never experienced before. I felt wonderful and as I cried and cried, the tears released the burden from my shoulders and I asked the Lord to come into my life and I repented of all my sins. When I came round I was lying on the floor, my coat filthy. What had happened? During all of the next week I walked round on a high. I couldn't wait for Sunday - I was a new being. John also gave his life to Christ that evening. We couldn't digest fully what had happened and wanted to know more.

Chapter 4

The following Sunday, Melissa sat next to me and touched my heart. She had a glow about her, a beauty. During the service they asked us to turn to a particular part of the Bible but I didn't have one!

The lady gave me her Bible and said that I could keep it, knowing that I didn't have one. No-one had ever given me anything in that way before. There was such love there.

Craig approached John again to say that they had a football team in the church and wondered if John would like to go training with them on Tuesday. John said that he would, and as they went back for coffee, Craig told John about an Alpha course that he was running the following evening. He was doing a brief course and would really like us to be involved.

The next evening, we went along to find that it was very low key and, thankfully, there was no three-course meal - just cake, which was easy to refuse. There were two other ladies, including one who had given her testimony on the previous Sunday, and Craig's wife. He gave us a book to read, then condensed a 12 week course into about 6 sessions. It was really good.

After that, we could not keep away. We attended every church service that we could. I was more reserved about receiving prayer, but someone would always spot me cowering and come and collect me. We went along to a gathering of many churches where the pastor picked me out and prayed over me. He knew that I was suffering, and knew I needed deliverance.

We progressed on to the Alpha course run by the church leader in the new year when we made many close friendships and learned much about Jesus, and experienced the Holy Spirit in a big way. The healing session really exposed to me how messy my life was and how much needed to be dealt with, and it was wonderful seeing new people giving their lives to the Lord. I thought that this must happen all of the time. Little did I know that it is like getting a camel through the eye of a needle!

CHAPTER FIVE

Light the fire in my soul

The most unhappy Christian is happier than the happiest non-Christian!

The statement above meant so much. The church leader repeated it on many occasions on our Alpha course and it stuck with John and I. We continued to go to church regularly and the Alpha course followed onto a Beta course. We were now in an established home-group and felt safe, we had been taken under someone' wings and nurtured, we loved the worship, and bought many CDs.

When we went to Craig's house we couldn't believe his whole collection was made up of Christian music. Our collection didn't have any Worship and Praise music and we thought we would never be the kind of people who were so 'church-lived'. Little did we know how dramatically our lives were going to change.

John and I were far from mature Christians, but we were very keen to learn and wanted to help on the following Alpha courses. The food issue wasn't a problem and I surprised myself, even doing some of the cooking on the courses, but I didn't eat the cakes or sweet things myself.

We both went through very messy divorces, and with Paul we had to call the police on various occasions. He still asked me to go back to him, even though he had a new partner, and he laughed at the fact that I had become a Christian and mocked it dreadfully. He kicked the door in on a couple of occasions and scared the children, which was wrong, but he still had legal rights as his name was still on the mortgage. I had to buy the house back from Paul. John and I were the recipients of a lot of abuse from the neighbours, and it was torture even to go out of the house.

We still had Lauren and Ellis to visit regularly and John and I vowed that this would never change. Gradually, Paul drifted out of Joshua and Daniel's life and eventually one day left a note to say that he was leaving and wasn't going to see them again. He asked me to say goodbye to them from him and they were heartbroken.

I felt guilty and blamed myself, but knew deep down that I had given Paul every opportunity to see the boys, but because of his own suffering childhood he could only see his own point of view. It was a sad time for the boys.

Joshua really grieved and even now we have to nurse the wounds. Daniel hates his father, and although we tell them that it is not their fault, nothing I say takes the pain away. More than anything, I do not want the boys to feel rejected in any way because I know from my own experience how damaging this can be. We try to encourage the boys by telling them that their father still loves them although he is unable to be with them, but the boys ask, "If he loves us, why doesn't he want to see us?". I find this difficult to answer.

The children adapted well to church life and because they have been through a lot in their little lives through no fault of their own, we have told all of them that, whatever happens, John and I will be together until death and that under no circumstances will we separate.

Six months after giving our lives to Jesus I was still living in this awful world of food domination. John didn't have a clue about how severe my problem was and I was still living in this secret world, sacrificing my time, money and energy to my binge-vomit cycle.

We had built up a number of friendships in the church by this time, but I still couldn't bring myself to talk to anyone about my problems. I was still afraid that John would leave me and I felt wrong about John and myself still sleeping together, convinced that because we weren't married this was a sin according to the Bible.

I was so confused. Why was I still suffering? I had invited Jesus Christ into my life and He is a healer, so why hadn't He taken this illness away from me like everyone had promised me He would? Why was I so insecure and hard on myself? So many questions with no answers. I prayed each night for God to take away my Bulimia but when I woke and looked to see if it was still there, sure enough it was.

One Sunday the church leader spoke about mind-sets, saying that people are trapped in their own little worlds and blame the enemy for the attacks on their lives. It is so easy to blame the enemy but some of the attacks are self-inflicted. Healing of mind-sets has to come from within because God would not dare to invade your right to choose, and a person has to want the change to come about. The leader agreed that change is frightening and uncomfortable, but to get the full glory of God we have to hand everything over to Him, no holding back by just giving Him the things we feel comfortable with.

He added that it may not happen overnight, and you may not be able to make these sacrifices of your own free will, but unless you get help, give up suffering in silence, and humble yourself and give that cry, you will not make that break to move forward with the Lord.

I was holding onto my Bulimia, unhappy, and a Christian suffering in silence. This sermon made me realise that it wasn't me who was giving my life to Christ, Christ had given His life for me, chosen me even before I was born. My destiny was already chosen, so instead of feeling sorry for myself, I should rejoice in what the Lord has done. He gave me life and set me free, so the rest is up to me - I have to confess to someone and tell the truth to release me from my eating disorder.

I realised then that God was going to use my experiences for the help of others and that I should not see my recovery process as a nightmare but look upon it as a blessing. I tried my hardest to explain the extent of my disorder to John, and how ashamed I was of the abuse I was inflicting on my body. I knew that my body is a temple for the Lord, so what right had I to mutilate it? I tried and tried with the help of the Lord to free myself, but before I knew it I was in the same trap. No matter how hard I tried to fight it, my flesh failed me again.

I had to get professional help because I knew that if we decided to move home, this might affect us. I made the excuse that we could not move because I wouldn't get life insurance, another limitation imposed by my problem. John told me not think like this, and gave me encouragement, saying that he wanted me to get better more than he wanted to move house.

John came to the GP with me, but the doctor didn't specialise in this field and didn't know much about eating disorders. He wanted to prescribe some anti-depressants, but I didn't feel depressed, I just needed help! I had experienced depression, but I wouldn't say this was depression, more desperation! I wanted to be cured. I refused the tablets.

The doctor referred me to the Mental Health Authority, and when I had an interview a few weeks later, I cried my heart out. They were very understanding, but no appointments were available to see anyone qualified for a few months at least, so I was referred to a dietician who weighed me each week and gave me guidelines for my eating habits. She asked me to write a diary of everything I ate and drank, but I could not do that at this stage.

I was taking so much time off work for hospital appointments that soon my employers would begin to ask questions and I was not ready for this. The job was boring and unsatisfactory, although I knew I should be grateful to have a job at all because there are many people who can't find work. I knew I was being ungrateful. The managing director was away at our sister office in the United States for most of the time and the time difference meant that most of my mornings were free and I would sit trying to find work, which was tedious, so I started taking binge foods into work. It was a vicious circle,

Living Behind the Mask

John and I talked about my situation and as he needed help in the office now due to the business expanding, and as I enjoyed that type of work, we looked at my joining him as a possibility. I was full time with my present employer and was tired of the boredom and the resulting binge-purge routine. I needed to feel stimulated to put my focus on something else. Yes, I had Jesus, but I was struggling.

The thought of eating a meal and keeping it down scared me. It was impossible for me to eat something cooked and keep it down. Hot food made me feel full and this made holidays, entertaining and socialising extremely difficult.

I was given a sheet of paper that helped to explain what a bodily function should be, and I feel it would be good to share this. It was written by an anonymous writer and likens our food intake to that of a wood-burning stove:

"Imagine that you are in a room. In the middle of the room is a round wood-burning stove. It is morning. The wood in the stove has burned down through the night and now the room feels chilly. You open the door of the stove and find that there are red-hot coals, and ashes left as waste from the wood.

In order to get the fire started you need to place a few small twigs on the coals. Perhaps you blow gently as you place the twigs on the coals. As a result, a small flame begins to develop and burn the twigs. As more twigs are placed in the stove the flame will increase. Then add a few small branches and eventually a couple of small logs to the burning fire. As the fire increases, a large portion, if not all, of the wood can burn.

Chapter 5

As the morning progresses, you may go to work or classes. Your fire has been burning, and the fuel is about burned up. It's about noon. You place a few small logs into the stove to allow the fire to continue burning into the afternoon. As you work and do your many activities, if the fire starts to go down, maybe about mid-afternoon, add another small log. Every time the fire starts to go down, or about every three hours, add another small log to the burning fire, depending on you need.

At about supper time, you may put a couple of logs on the fire, allowing it to burn well into the night. You could use a hard wood, which burns slowly, instead of paper, which burns fast. Your room is warm, concentration was good throughout the day, and you may feel strong as you go to bed.

The next morning once again the room is a little chilly. Your coals are red hot and you have wood to fuel the coals, but you decide that you are not going to put any fuel into the stove. You head off to work or classes. At first all seems fine. As the morning passes, your coals get weaker. Your concentration begins to fade. By afternoon you may find yourself less patient, more irritable, and constantly thinking about fuel. The temperature in the room gets colder. The coals are weak grey embers.

You feel weak and dizzy. As you enter the room in desperation and with a sense of no control, you take several large logs and stuff them into the stove at once. You binge. Those logs sit in the stove smouldering. Most of them are unable to burn.

A body is like the wood-burning stove. The fire is like the metabolic rate. When you get up in the morning, your metabolic rate is lower, but it is already red hot, to get started.

When you think of food from now on, try replacing the word "calories" with "fuel". Calories are fuel. Fuelling the fire inside your body provides you with much needed energy, strength, and potential for greater control.

Just like the wood-burning stove, it is important to get your metabolic fire going in the morning while your coals are primed to start. Each bite of food you eat is like placing some twigs on the coals to start your fire.

You could eat small amount of food throughout the morning, or fuel your stove by putting all the twigs in at one time in the morning. About two or three hours later you may need to place more fuel in your stove to keep the fire going. (You may feel a gurgling sensation in your stomach. That is your message that your fire is beginning to go down). Add more fuel to the fire or the fire will die down. Once the fire gets going it burns best if you put something substantial in it for lunch. It doesn't have to be a huge amount, just a couple of small logs to keep your fire going into the afternoon.

Just as two logs burn better than one, two types of food often digest better than one food type alone. Your body uses different foods to help in digestion. As you go through the day, when you feel that gurgling sensation again, know it's a sensation that your fire is going down. It is time to put more fuel in your fire. If you don't get the gurgling sensations, fuel your fire about every two to three hours, regularly, as you would add fuel to a stove. Eat a little to maintain your fire.

At supper, you might need to put two or three logs into your stove so that they burn well and into the night to keep you warm so you can rest.

If your fire is going well, the temptation to put more fuel in your fire before bedtime is much less, because your body feels stronger and more satisfied, more in control.

If you delay and do not fuel your fire throughout the day, it is more difficult to get your fire started; you force your metabolic rate to go down. When you finally give in and eat, or binge, later in the day when your coals are weak, a larger portion of the binge goes to fat because your metabolic rate if not yet high enough to burn up the food. The very thing you fear comes true. Eating after fasting could initially encourage your body to send more food to fat. If you start fuelling your fire in the morning and keep your fire going all day, just like the wood-burning stove, larger portions, if not all, the fuel can burn up.

But if you get your fire started and burning well and then you put an extra piece of wood into the fire. Does that mean that the extra wood will just lie there and not burn or turn to fat? Not necessarily. Because the fire is already burning well, the extra wood makes the fire higher and you get overheated (hypothermic). You burn up the excess fuel more easily when your fire is going well than when you eat nothing and go a long time without fuelling. It is harder to burn up excess fuel if no fire has been started.

So when you eat, each morning if you struggle with breakfast think, "I need to get my fire started" and "Each bite is a twig beginning to burn up and give me strength for the day". Imagine how fuel can be added to your fire throughout the day. As you get your fire going in the morning think about the type of fuel you need.

Exercise is like putting billows on a fire, making the fire hotter and burning up the fuel faster. But just as you can fan a fire too long and blow it out, too much exercise can bring down your metabolic rate. Too little and too much exercise is not as healthy as an amount that allows the fire to intensify and burn the fuel well.

Think also about your spiritual life, instead if you don't top up that fire each day with a little prayer or worship, the Bible, Christian meetings, the fire will die down, you need to have a positive spiritual life, keeping connected to the fire (God), keep fanning that flame, he will eventually make you whole.

You need to feed the fire with the word of God and burn all the waste of the day away to cleanse yourself again, a furnace burns rubbish and just leaves ashes, you need to blow the ashes away and continue your daily walk with Christ, feed your relationship."

I handed in my notice at work and started to work with John. More than anything he desired me to get cured and was pleased that I was going to see the dietician voluntarily. She taught me that I needed to eat small amounts regularly - at the time the most I could eat was toast and the food I actually consumed and let digest was minimal. I was still hopping on and off the scales, and unconscious of the fact that I was calorie counting. If I ate over 600 calories per day, I felt guilty and it would usually result in a bigger binge as a punishment to myself. My study of diet books and cookery books contributed to this.

I eventually got an appointment with the psychiatrist who asked me many intrusive questions about my life history, most of which is described earlier in this book. He asked me how Bulimia had affected my life, and what damage had been caused physically to my body. I really didn't know entirely what the side effects were, and only knew that I hadn't been a very well person and that it had destroyed relationships, and that people died from eating disorders.

He described the corrosion of the enamel on my teeth, which is very evident; yellowness on the nails due to induced vomiting; swelling of the glands and stomach; stopping of the menstrual cycle; abdominal pains; general digestive problems like constipation or damage to the bowel muscles; difficulty in sleeping; feeling cold if underweight causing a fine hair over the body; muscle weakness; brittle bones causing easy breakages; depression; fainting; low concentration; and panic attacks.

He scared me when he said that if I continued I could cause damage to my stomach lining, even rip it open; the irregularity of my heartbeats could cause a heart attack; kidney damage could lead to kidney failure; vomiting could cause damage to my throat and could cause a tear in the oesophagus; I might have epileptic fits; and I could cause an imbalance in body water, salt and mineral content.

More than anything, I wanted someone to say, "give it to me, I will dispose of it for you", but this wasn't going to happen! I looked at it more like a terminal disease, something which wriggles through your body and you hope and pray it can be cut out, and although you will be left with scars, you would free to live even though there would be a constant reminder from the marks on your body. Realising that I could save myself from the more severe side effects, I needed to have this problem cut away, but the cutting had to be in my mind and needed a lot of surgery from within, as well as guidance from a professional.

He looked at my case notes and asked me what I preferred, a one-to-one treatment or a group session. I didn't feel capable of making a decision but thought that in a group it would be too general. I wanted to see a result so maybe the personal therapy would suit me. He asked if I would like some anti-depressants, saying that they helped to stop the cravings, but I needed to know that I could do it by myself and didn't take the medication.

Six weeks later, I saw a psychiatric nurse who was very understanding. She asked me to monitor for the next week everything I ate, drank and thought before during and after food, including all binge foods. I went out of there thinking "I am not going to binge again, I cannot show another human being exactly how much I consume in a day, she would be horrified" - there couldn't be anyone as bad as me!

I lasted until the evening when I thought, "Well, I don't have to start the diary sheets until tomorrow, I must get one more binge in". It lasted all evening - tomorrow was the start of a new day. On the next day, the same cravings came and were too much to bear, so I gave in and didn't want to write the food content down.

I hated myself because I didn't realise how much I was consuming in such a short space of time. I gave in time and time again, leaving me feeling that I was a total failure. What would this woman think of me? I can't even produce a diary and she will think I haven't even tried, and what was the point in her giving up her time to counsel me if I couldn't even be bothered to try.

I went back the following week, a total failure, feeling worse than the week before. She was very understanding and said that she realised that it was very painful and difficult to do, so again she asked me to go away and write down everything, explaining that she wanted to see some form of pattern or trigger foods, to see if she could identify something that I couldn't.

Chapter 5

I did go away and managed to keep a diary of everything for a week, but I was terrified in case someone would see it. I was very possessive of my sheets and very ashamed of what was being written. I could not believe the severity of my problem, and although I knew it was bad, I didn't realise until I saw it on paper how ill I was. I hated monitoring myself, of revealing that I was guilty of wasting my life, slowly killing myself, punishing myself for silly things, guilty of holding onto Bulimia, trying to hand it over to God but then taking it back into my safe little world.

I soon recognised that Bulimia was my control button, my coping mechanism. I had had a stressful life and needed an escape. There were so many things in my life over which I had no authority. At least I had the overall decision on my eating and no-one could interfere, it was all mine, and if anyone dared to comment or criticise, they had no rights. Bulimia was for me - I was captured by this private life which no-one knew fully, and I didn't want them to.

I could push away all my problems by bingeing, then spit all my problems out, releasing the daily stresses. I would pile them up in a heap inside my body then crush down further any hurts, emotions and pain.

I think of it as a full rubbish bin where more trash accumulates when you add this waste into the bin, pushing it down harder with your feet, compressing the compost at the bottom where it is rotting, and the stench if the lid is lifted could signal to others that it is safer to leave the lid on. But a bin needs to be emptied eventually ...

I needed to put my focus into something else - Bulimia needs to fade away. The fire in my soul needed to be lit and I wanted the Lord to be my fire-starter and for the flame to be concealed by God so that the Bulimia could not blow it out. The Lord was stirring a passion inside me, my focus fully needed to be Him, not food, not my partner, not my children, not my house, first and foremost must be God. God made the promise that He will set me free, it will take time, but I can do it with His help. Bulimia had been with me for many years and I needed to train myself to be normal, but I knew now it wouldn't happen overnight.

Here is a monitoring sheet for November 1996. I destroyed the ones previous to this date:

Food Diary: Saturday, 9th November, 1996

Time	Drink and Food Intake	Room	
8.15am	Cup of tea	Bathroom	Weight 6 stones 12 pounds – lost a pound
8.45am	2 slices toast, vitamin tablet	Bedroom	Must eat breakfast
1.00pm	2 cups of tea, toasted sandwich, pasties, lemonades, bag crisps, scone, spoons beans, rice & meat	Kitchen	John was going out for afternoon I knew I wouldn't stop.* Wanted to get rid of it but could get some more in

	sauce, lemonade, Mars bar, biscuits, Bounty bar, 4 Weetabix.		
2.10pm	2 lemonades		*Vomited, needed to wash myself out. Weight 6 stones 13 pounds. Knew food still inside
2.15pm	2 lemonades		*Vomited. Still felt bloated Weight 7 stones?
3.30pm	Half can Coke	Car	Felt like screaming
5.30pm	Cup black coffee	Mum's	*Wanted to get home and binge
6.00pm	Burger & Coke	McDonalds	*Could have carried on but resisted, thought bad but shrugged it off
7.00pm	2 bottles lager, Chinese ordered	Lounge	Knew I couldn't eat Chinese
8.00pm	Chinese take-away, lager	Lounge	*How was I going to get rid of it?
9.00pm	5 scones, cup of tea, lemonade	Kitchen	*Needed to get rid of it

9.20pm			Vomited. Felt disgusting, useless, felt full still, I
11.00pm	lemonade	Lounge	wish it would all go away, I hate these feelings!

F = Feeling, represented by *. This is when I am feeling uncomfortable or wanting to binge.

This was an average day at the time and I was advised to increase my daily intake. I was taking vitamin tablets to boost the minerals in my body, obviously I was lacking the important nutrients in my body and I don't know whether it was just in my mind, but I did feel better after introducing multivitamins.

Over the months, I found myself opening up more and more to my counsellor. I was confessing everything and the monitoring sheets became a matter of course. Slowly, the binges cut down, and though it was still daily, I started to build up my self esteem. My visits to the mental health centre were still frequent and there were occasional visits to the hospital to keep a record of my progress.

John and I were together 24 hours a day and we loved being in each other's company. Unfortunately, I still could not open up to John. I wanted to tell him everything, but couldn't.

I was encouraged to know that I was gradually recovering, but John had been unaware of the degree to which I had been infested with this disease, and was still unaware.

Chapter 5

We decided that we had to move out of the house, which was difficult because John still shared the mortgage with his ex-wife. We prayed about it and put the house on the market. It was my worst time of year - Christmas! I hated Christmas, so much food, everywhere you go there is food, visit a friend and you are offered food, turn on the television, food (adverts are the worst), supermarket shelves filled with chocolates, mince pies, Christmas puddings - the list is endless, binge food galore.

Traditionally, Christmas is a time for enjoying fine foods, wines, family gatherings, and holiday time to relax. To an eating disorder sufferer, this is one of the worst nightmares because the festive season is filled with pressures from all angles.

Being a very generous person, I love to spoil people, so I go over the top, especially with the children's gifts, maybe to compensate for not spending as much time with them as I would like to. My biggest obstacle is the Christmas food and drink because, being so organised, I buy in bulk and months in advance, which is a mistake because I have to replace half of it before Christmas even arrives.

This particular Christmas was even more stressful than usual because we had people coming to view the house and had to make sure everything was spotlessly clean and in its place, the children had to behave, and there was so much pressure. We had already been through many stressful times over this past year and a half, moving jobs for me twice, setting up the company, divorce, and now moving house. I think that maybe we were pre-meditating a nervous breakdown!

Luckily, the first people to come and look round the house wanted it and they put in an offer, so off we went looking for a house to suit us.

This was a difficult task but eventually we did find a house, a much bigger house in a nicer neighbourhood and where the boys didn't have to move school. We felt that they didn't need any more disruptions in their young lives.

We moved in March 1997 and although the mortgage was double that on our old home, it felt nice and it was ours - a fresh start. I resolved not contaminate this house with my horrible habits.

However, the vomiting cycle slipped in again and because the toilets did not flush very well I was afraid that I would block them up. John thought that I was almost there in my recovery and I still resisted telling anyone in the church.

I had started a prayer triplet with two other women, Charlotte and Anita, but I wasn't being honest. We were praying for everything else, and becoming really close, so what would they think if I told them?

The Lord had given us so much. He was shining in my life and people noticed a difference in me. My mother and father thought that I had changed, and Joseph even said I was nice now - he now had a steady girlfriend and they have a baby whom I love dearly, with another on the way.

I began to focus on my childhood and all the strains and arguments I had brought into the family. I deeply regretted all the anguish and pain I had given to my parents because they didn't deserve it. With our own children, we don't know how the last year has affected them, and can only hope and pray that they can be open and talk to us, and that we can create a loving Christian atmosphere.

CHAPTER SIX

The 30 Day Vision

I started to read books which had been recommended by my psychiatrist and began to have an understanding of myself, although I still didn't know who I really was, or what my natural thoughts, ideas, and desires were. I realised that I had the same ailments as most people with eating disorders and soon recognised that Anorexia, Bulimia and compulsive eating were all connected, with many similarities. John and I began to argue and generally weren't getting on and we came to the conclusion that it was mainly about the decoration and furniture in the new house. Realising that we had totally different tastes and opinions, we managed to compromise on decisions. It stemmed from the fact that the old house had been mine and my ex-husbands, and this house was ours. John said that he didn't have any desire for the old house because in this house his opinion was valid. I still felt insecure about our relationship, although I knew deep down that John had given up everything for me and that both of our lives were now totally different, but there were still doubts in my mind.

A few months later I revealed to John that I needed to feel more secure, but he wasn't ready to marry me and he made that quite clear, which upset me and made me feel rejected. I began to put up my defences again and blocked my feelings in fear that the relationship might break down, and in my foolishness prepared myself for the worst. Eventually, it came to a head and John proposed to me. We went out and bought the ring the same day while John's parents baby-sat for the children. It was the end of May 1997.

Everything went quickly after that. The date had been set for 30th

August 1997 and with so many plans and preparations to be made, we had a friend, Jackie, helping us with the organisation. It was so exciting and this time it would be for keeps.

We went on a marriage course with our church leader and his wife and were encouraged to practice what we had learned on the course in our relationship, so that it had the correct grounding for a Christian marriage.

The basics of never putting the marriage on the line, like not saying hurtful words like "I wish I had never married you!", or anything similar, was a condition never to be broken. Rules had to be made, boundaries set: never go to sleep without correcting an argument; respect each other as individuals. The course was very good and, above all, our covenant would be for life - a covenant together put before God. Our wedding would be special and we wanted it to be inspiring to all the non-Christian guests and for them to feel the Holy Spirit's presence.

My eating improved immeasurably as my self-esteem lifted. I felt whole with John, and more and more prayers were being answered. The more I understood about my illness, the easier it became to deal with. My time was occupied with the wedding preparations, and I was beginning to see glimpses of the true me - and liking who I was. I was quite annoyed when the dressmakers were trying to tell me that I needed a size 4 dress which was the equivalent to our size petite 6. I saw myself as a size 10, and they agreed to order it, but when it arrived they were proved to be correct as it was too big and it needed alterations.

My counsellor did urge me to be careful, especially when all the excitement died down. We had experienced so much anxiety and stress in these last couple of years and she was worried about what would keep me going when it all stopped. I hadn't even thought of this and as far as I was concerned my eating habits had improved and I felt better in my mind, more confident.

We were leading quite a hectic social life, but it was good. We went on holiday and had barbecues and parties. We have lots of good friends and we were strong as a couple.

I was trying to please John all of the time, to have my hair the way he liked it, served him, and tried to be the best partner I could be. I thought he wouldn't like me if I was fat; he liked my body at the moment. I was no longer looking at what I wanted or what would please me.

The church set up a 30 day month of prayer and fasting for revival and a rota was set up with various church members to lead the prayer evenings. Fasting could be food, alcohol, TV, sex, or anything which would be a sacrifice to give up for a month.

Initially I thought about the food because to fast for a whole month would be easy, but I knew this would appeal to the Anorexic mind! I knew it was sensible to choose something else, even though the temptation was there to starve myself, but I knew it would not be for the prayer, it would be for me. The reason for the prayer month was because it was a countdown to a Christian Concert headed by various Christian bands, and with special guest leaders from across the nations.

In June, we went to the concert, the 'Champion of the World' concert in Wembley stadium. This was a significant time because in the previous year when we crammed into the Wembley Arena, Noel Richards had had a vision that one day there would be a Champion of the World celebration at Wembley Stadium, and here we were. We had also walked on the March for Jesus in 1996, waving banners and singing praises to the Lord through the streets.

It shook me up to recognise that, without my realising it, I had been making Bulimia the champion of my life, and it was not a champion at all because the Lord was gaining the victory and the Champion of the world is Jesus. 45,000 people packed the stadium and sang, danced, celebrated and gave worship to the Lord of Lords and King of Kings. People had travelled from all over the world to be there and the atmosphere was electrifying - God's spirit was there in full glory.

It had rained solidly all week and had been one of the wettest Junes on record. The weather forecast was torrential rain, but when the concert started at Wembley, it was dry, although all around it was still raining. What a Miracle!

I realised then that God can do anything. If He can change the weather (only a drop of a miracle) He can cure me of my illness. I knew I had to trust in Him. God gave a vision to one man to praise and worship at Wembley Stadium and he obeyed and the vision became a reality. God had given me a vision that I would be cured and God would use my vision to heal others through my experiences, so how dare I disobey God's wishes?

The months passed very quickly, the replies flooding in and almost 300 people accepted the invitation to the church and 150 to the wedding reception. We booked the honeymoon suite in the hotel where the reception was being held and booked the honeymoon - an all inclusive package for a week in Tunisia. The thing that scared me was the eat-or-drink-as-much-as-you-like part of the package, but on the positive side, the food won't cost us a fortune, especially if most of it ends up down the toilet!

We had the stag do and hen night and before we knew it the wedding day was upon us. John went to stay with his sister on the night before the wedding, everything was ready, and my parents came to stay. I went to have a facial, and then people arrived from everywhere including my friend Jackie. Her daughter Sue was to be matron of honour. All the children were excited, people were running around like headless chickens, but amongst them all I felt very relaxed.

The hairdresser arrived to do everyone's hair and we drank wine and enjoyed the day. The beautician arrived and transformed me with perfect make-up and I was as pleased as I could be with the way I looked. I was determined that even if everything didn't go perfectly and there were hiccups, it wouldn't ruin our day.

My Dad said how proud he was of me, of how beautiful his little girl looked and Mum screamed and burst into tears, saying how lovely I looked. I wasn't quite expecting this kind of response.

The photographer came and took some shots of the children and me with my matron of honour and my parents. Then the cars arrived and took everyone to the church, leaving me with my father. It was a very special time and I started getting butterflies in my stomach. It dawned on me that what was happening and all the planning had been worth it. It would be a day never to be forgotten.
We arrived at the church and everything was perfect - the music,

the ceremony. It was a real day of celebration with songs perfect for the day with so many friends and family there. We were both very touched. "Mrs Havell" - it sounded funny. The children were very good.

After the ceremony, we went on to the wedding reception which, again, was perfect. John and I finally sat down at 1 am on the 31st August and he was so handsome, looking really smart in his suit. We had three hours before our lift would arrive to take us to the airport! It had been a long day, but I hadn't thought about food all day and it was a day of happiness and a day of freedom.

I was in love with a wonderful man - I had found my knight in shining armour.

When we turned on the television at 4 am the newsreader was telling us that Lady Diana had been in a car accident and had been injured but was stable. We drove to the airport then and caught the plane to Tunisia. At the Tunisian airport rumours were going around the air terminal that Diana had died. I couldn't believe it and felt a real sense of loss. This young woman of high rank had suffered from Bulimia, but had found happiness in her life only to have her life was taken away prematurely. I had found happiness too, but I was killing myself willingly. I must do something drastic to get better.

The weather was awful, but we met a lot of people on our honeymoon and it was though people could see something different in us because they flocked to us like bees round a honey pot.

They must have been able to see the Lord in us because it couldn't have been anything I was doing. My eating was totally diabolical - I was punishing myself for having this joy in my life when I wasn't worth it.

Coming home, we couldn't wait to see the children and they were so pleased to see us. A child's love is unconditional and God's love for us is like this - no matter what we say or do nothing can make God love us more than he does.

The children helped us to open all of our wonderful wedding gifts. People had been so generous and I had to face facts, people do like us and no matter what I think of myself, I have friends and family who do love me. God loved me so much that He gave his only Son for me, and if I was the only person on this earth Jesus would have died for my sins. Jesus was given as a living sacrifice to cleanse me and set me free, I had to believe it!

We had a dilemma with the boys. They assumed that because John and I were now married their names would automatically change and we tried to explain that we couldn't do this without their father's permission, but if this was what they wanted we would see what we could do. It was understandable that they should want the same surname as the rest of us because they accepted John as their father, but knew they had another dad somewhere.

The business was very successful and we were expanding. It was very challenging and enjoyable, but a couple of weeks after returning from our honeymoon we had some terrible news. My granddad had died and my mother was on holiday so I went to stay with my grandmother until my mother returned. I missed John and the children terribly but I knew my grandmother's need was greater.

On the day of the funeral, my uncle collapsed and he was diagnosed as having lung cancer. It brought home to me that I had to alter the way I thought about myself - I had my health but I was damaging myself because my eating was slipping back into old habits.

I decided to contact the self-help group I had attended before, but they no longer existed. However, the person who had held the groups had realised that there was a need for eating disorders in the Colchester area and he had set up an eating disorder centre, so I went to see him. I was very open about everything and it was very welcoming. I soon recognised how far I had come in my recovery because there were people a lot worse off than me, following the same patterns as I had two years ago. This was encouraging and I wanted to help them. I continued to see my psychiatrist.

I read somewhere that some eating disorders can be triggered by certain types of food, especially foods to which a person is allergic. I have suffered for a number of years with a skin condition which leaves me feeling very itchy and when my skin becomes inflamed and blotchy or goes very dry and cracked, it looks a lot like eczema. I have used many ointments and creams to calm the skin, but always after a while I would become immune to the creams and my skin would revert to its poor condition.

After quite a lot of visits to my GP, I was told that the condition was caused by an allergy, most probably to a certain type of food, and to find the offending trigger would involve a long process of elimination. Well, I tried this, torturing myself by cutting out foods which I eat quite often and it was terrible because I craved for the foods that I cut out and it was sending me crazy.

My skin was at its worst and I spoke to a friend who suggested I go for a Vega test to find out what I was allergic to. I had never heard of this test before and I don't really know what I was expecting, but we went into this lady's basement where there were books everywhere, a couch and a seat, a very professional set up. The lady told me to sit down and asked me to take off my footwear. A metal machine was set up on a bench with two wires coming out of it, one wire having a metal pen attached and the other a metal bar. I had never seen anything like it before.

I was told to hold the metal bar at the same time as the lady held my left foot, and she told me she would test me by touching my toe with the metal pen and this would show the reading on the Vega machine. If there is a loud high pitched sound and the meter reading turns fully to the right, it signifies no reaction, but if the meter has a low reading and it is more of a buzzing sound, this indicates that there is an allergic reaction.

She had trays full of what I can only describe as small samples of perfume. They contained lots of different substances, but if there proved to be an allergic reaction she considered specific products.

I discovered that I had a strong reaction to every kind of perfume product, most make-up products, smoke, grass, pollen and exhaust fumes. It wasn't so much what I was eating, it was what I was inhaling or putting on my skin.

I was quite relieved to find out what I was allergic to - at least now I had something to work with. I was very surprised to discover exactly how many products contain perfume and I had to throw out my deodorant, shampoo, hairspray and make-up. Some of the creams which I was putting on to cure my skin contained perfume and were aggravating my condition. I looked ten years older!

I knew I must move forward and do something positive, so I confessed to the girls in my prayer triplet that I had an eating disorder. What a breakthrough! I was beginning to open up to more and more people. My confidence was building and my feelings towards myself were changing. We were welcomed into church membership as a family and as the church prayed for us, I had these words of wisdom given to me:

"Ella, you have been given wisdom, strength and riches to
use in the name of the Father who names you as His own.
This is time of healing and growth before you go further,
study the word and look for the Father's wisdom in all that you do.

Healing comes before growth. Please heal first.

Allow healing. Much fruit will be borne through the
guidance given to others".

This confirmed to me my direction.

We decided as a family that John would adopt the boys, so we went along to our solicitor - we were becoming quite regular clients! The solicitors advised us to change the children's names then go for a resident order in six months' time which would enable John legally to have guardianship over the boys if anything were to happen to me. We had to cover ourselves from all angles and had wills drawn up and set up pensions.

Christmas was coming up - the first Christmas I wasn't dreading, and we were going to my parent's house so it wasn't necessary for me to stock up on the Christmas binge foods. I felt good about this. Christmas was a lovely day and we were free to celebrate Jesus's birth without the clutter of food issues.

In the build up to the New Year, I was determined that I was not going to make a resolution this year, so many times had I said "Tomorrow, I will never binge again!" and was doomed to fail. I was taking each day as it came but still bingeing once a day, although my thought patterns had changed and my self-esteem had risen. I had forgiven everyone in my past and I just had to sort out my eating irregularity - or so I thought.

On 1st January 1998, I knew the Lord was with me and that this was going to be my year of freedom. I felt God saying that He had freed me from eating disorders, and it was up to me now. I could feel an eruption inside me, something big was going to happen this year. I didn't know what it was but knew the time was nearing for the Lord to use my eating disorder for His purpose.

I had taken practical steps to improve my eating but I still wasn't there, only taking baby steps on my road to recovery, but slowly I was breaking out of my vicious cycle.

I had been patient with myself and the results were showing - my monitor sheets read as if a different person was writing them.

More people were getting involved with me in the eating disorder area, and, without my knowing, a little team was gathering with support for me. The Lord was revealing people to me who were also suffering with eating problems.

John knew I was getting better, but his perception was that I was bingeing and vomiting once a month maybe, not once a day! How was I going to tell him? One night we were lying in bed when John plucked up the courage to ask how my eating was going. Ordinarily he wouldn't ask for fear of my raging at him, but my eyes welled up with tears and I told him I was bingeing daily.

He went silent and slipped into sleep, but the next day he was distant towards me and I felt rejected, thinking he must be repulsed by me, but, on the contrary, he was thinking and praying. He felt the Lord saying to him very clearly that, like the 30 day prayer and fasting up to the Champion of the World Concert, I needed a 30 day month of prayer! It is a scientific fact that a habit can be changed in a matter of 30 consecutive days. It may not be cured, but the thought patterns can be broken.

We talked a lot over the next few days and I sensed strongly that I was approaching my final hurdle. We talked about my most vulnerable times and what I thought would help me, and we agreed that I had to be totally honest from now on. John decided to take charge of the kitchen and prepare, cook and serve the meals. The only thing he was unsure about was the decision about what meals to cook each night.

I also had to plan my daily intake of food. I chose a basic nutritional diet and had to be creative on this, to break my theory about good and bad foods. I also agreed that I must not let myself get hungry, I must snack in between meals, or try to eat every three to four hours, and hopefully this should curb the cravings. I was to keep my monitor sheets up-to-date and to hand, available for anyone to see.

Basic daily intake

| **Breakfast** | - | Bowl cereals with milk |
| or | | 2 slices toast with a suitable spread |

| **Mid Morning** | | Scone or piece fruit |

Lunch	-	2 slices bread to make sandwich, packet crisps
or		Bowl of soup with toast followed by yoghurt
or		Beans on toast followed by fruit

| **Mid-afternoon** | - | Cake or chocolate bar |

| **Evening Meal** | - | Meal with potato, pasta or rice with meat or fish or egg or cheese With vegetables, or salad |

| **Bedtime** | - | 2 biscuits Or 1 slice toast |

I knew that I must try to eat the majority of my food before 6 pm and John dished up the meals aware of the fact that my concept of normal eating was far from ordinary, and my portion control was abnormal. I agreed not to weigh myself.

John made an appointment to see Louise, one of our church leaders, and they had a prayer evening, then quickly a rota was drawn up so that there were at least three people there each evening to pray for me during my critical time which we had established to be between 6.30 - 7.30 pm. It was all well organised, but John was shocked to find he was leading the prayer month and it was scary for both of us.

We made preparations and were given some pictures by various people to help the healing process. The one which seemed the most significant was a picture of John as a radiant large white shiny pillar, with me as a beautiful red rose twining round the pillar. The rose would be pruned back and would grow again more stronger and more lovely than before, so that eventually the pillar could be removed and I could stand on my own two feet.

The prayer month began on 25th January and lasted until 23rd February.

Chapter 7

CHAPTER SEVEN

No Fishing!

I had managed to get through the whole of Sunday without bingeing, which was a miracle in itself. Sunday evening came round very quickly and we had an open house, the lounge packed with people. I was overwhelmed and touched by the dedication and commitment that people were prepared to give for me - there were approximately 40 people involved in praying for me, and where there were circumstances where some people could not come to our house, some friends prayed in their own homes or in small groups.

John started the evening by sharing his burdens of my illness and his vision for the consecutive 30 days of prayer. He explained that he would be leading the prayer evenings, and that some strict rules had been drawn up and these were made clear. The people attending the prayer evenings were to be only a support for John and must be sensitive to the way we were feeling; anyone not on the rota should ring before the prayer time; and decisions could not be made much in advance because the power of the Holy Spirit would be the main leader; confidentiality must not be broken; intercessors should arrive promptly at 6.30 pm and leave at 7.30 pm unless there was a need for them to stay or arrive early.

I felt comfortable about all of this, and then it was my turn to expose my life totally. I felt stripped naked and very vulnerable, but felt safe in doing so. I didn't want people to feel sorry for me, I wanted to reveal everything so that people knew what they were dealing with. We opened up to questioning and answered the best way we knew how.

John explained that the structure for the month would be that the first week would be a week focusing on love and acceptance of myself (horror); the second and third week would be two weeks of deliverance; and the fourth week would be a week of grace.

I knew I was on the last hurdle of my eating disorder, but I was told that I wouldn't need to jump that last hurdle because it would be more like kicking that hurdle aside. God wouldn't put me through anything I couldn't handle, He would be at my side. I have lost too much dignity in my life. God will be gentle and graceful to me, showering me with love and peace.

I said I couldn't understand why God didn't heal me instantly, why He had left it for this period of time, and Lucy explained that it was like an onion - all the outer layers are being peeled back and absolute freedom will come when all the peel has been removed and the core can be plucked out, but if the core is taken out before the layers have been dealt with, the layers can re-grow around the core.

We prayed in a group and, with John and I standing in the middle feeling very uncomfortable, we were told to focus on the image of the white pillar with the rose. I was told to use John's strength and sap him, using his faith to get healed because John had the strength for both of us.

Trevor had a picture of a maze full of mirrors like those you see at the seaside. I had been wandering around the maze and seeing myself distorted. God is now showing me the exit signs. I am a daughter of the most high God, part of the royal priesthood, I am a princess, I must keep my head held high, the Lord had placed a robe of righteousness over me.

Chapter 7

It was suggested at the end of the evening that I bathe myself. I was feeling exhausted and unclean and even though the prayers had been very low key, my stomach was stirring and I wanted to collapse. After having a bath, I felt refreshed and peaceful, although usually I would avoid having a bath because I always thought I was fat and was reluctant to look at the distorted image I had of my body enlarged by the water. I stepped out of the bathtub a new person. It was incredible.

Everyone was very caring and compassionate to our feelings and a diary was kept of the following 30 days of prayer, together with my food monitoring sheets. I agreed that trigger foods would be eliminated as much as possible, and alcohol was allowed only in moderation. We cancelled appointments and re-scheduled our usually busy lives for this month. Our lifestyle had to change. Each evening was planned so that we would give an outline of the day's events, have a discussion about it, and pray into the areas which had arisen.

26th January 1998

The day has been tough and it has been a battle. I have been feeling very agitated and my mind has been very much preoccupied with food, so I have had to concentrate hard and focus on the Lord.

The binge cravings were terrible but I knew that if I persevered the feelings would go. John was a tower of strength and he responded with a positive reply to all the attacks I gave him.

We had to eat before everyone came round and I felt I had eaten too much. I had snacked all day and had three meals. I was nervous. At 6.30pm three intercessors arrived, Rebecca, Jackie, and Diane, and I was told to keep focused on God through this next month. There was a strong sense of Jesus wanting to reveal His Father's Heart to me.

Jackie said I was like a syringe and I must not absorb the negative things any more, but instead I must soak up God's love and retain it ready to release it to others when the time is right.

The prayers started and I folded my arms, clutching tight to my stomach The pain inside was frightening, but it was explained that there were demons trying to manifest. John prayed to "Stop it!" and there was a sense of the enemy trying to distract, to deter me from focusing on God.

Jackie asked me to open up my arms to the Lord and He would fill them with love. They felt the Lord saying,

"I have made you and you are very good! As I fill your arms, your heart, your spirit with my love for you, I will also fill them with people who need my love which you can pour out to them.

As I fill your open arms, so you will pour my love onto others, spreading my word and love. Do not close your arms against my love, keep them ever open and raised to accept my love. Ella, I love you and am always with you".

I was tired now, had my bath and looked back on the day. I had made it through day two.
(Psalm 31: 7-8) (Psalm 23)(Romans 12:3)

27th January 1998

We went to France today with some friends, Andy and Rachel. it was a lovely sunny day and I had made a packed lunch but felt as though maybe I should have stopped eating because I had the urge to carry on and binge but then made myself feel comfortable with what I had eaten. I knew I had to live with this and, realistically, I hadn't eaten any more than anyone else. We went to the supermarket and were overwhelmed by the amount of food around - everything was so cheap. We bought binge foods - shouldn't have done. The thoughts about food were horrible and I started planning binges in my head, but I conquered them.

Andrew stayed after returning from France. Jackie, Doug and Charlotte arrived and we shared the day. Obviously it had been a long struggle of a day. Andrew said that I had a banner over me which is love, it is time to put the banner in the ground and mark my area, and to put a notice on the flag 'God's territory and the enemy is not welcome!'.

Doug felt the Lord said "Ella, listen to me as I call your name - because I love you. Ella, Ella, Ella, Ella!" He suggested that I look in a mirror and tell myself "I love YOU". I didn't feel that I would ever be able to do this.

Rebecca saw me like a pearl which starts off with a grain of sand entering into the oyster shell with the oyster, then the oyster coats this grit to stop the sand irritating it, and eventually the oyster leaves its shell, leaving a precious gem. The grit is the eating disorder, I am the oyster coating it, working with it, until eventually it will be used for something beautiful. I must use my annoyance to anoint others.

Charlotte advised John and I to find strength in each other as this will bring us closer together, but the battle belongs to the Lord and He will have the victory.

(Isaiah 43: 2-4) (Ephesians 3:16-19) (Isaiah 41) (Matthew 4) (1 Corinthians 10:13) (2 Corinthians 10:4-5)

28th January 1998

I sat and ate breakfast with my sons. I felt relaxed about today but quite ratty with Joshua and Daniel and this made me feel guilty. Got very agitated with John - I just need some time alone, all these people were getting to be too much. I needed to get out of the office and keep myself busy so this is what I did. Ate with John in the evening when he made the meal. It was lovely and I found myself enjoying it.

A quiet night tonight. Jackie came along to pray and I took a major step forward and took command over my body when the Spirit manifested. John prayed for a binding of the Spirit and the release of my throat so that I could speak because until now I hadn't been able to pray myself. I spoke "Jesus, Jesus, Jesus" and spoke in the spiritual gift of tongues. The evening was very much about grace.

I saw an ugly black being inside my stomach, all shiny and slimy and it was laughing at me. It felt like a monster chasing its tail around in my belly and I had a real feeling of hatred towards it. I didn't necessarily believe in abortion but I wanted to abort this creature for it never to return.

God is working in my life, no bingeing, I praise His name.
(Psalm 40) (Psalm 145:8-9;13)

29th January 1998

I had a very restless night, so I got up and did the ironing. John made toast with loads of butter but this made me feel sick so I scraped off the butter then ate the toast even though my appetite was now gone. The food I had eaten over the last few days was getting easier to handle but the truth of the matter was that I just wasn't hungry. I had to force myself to eat at lunchtime, but I went out for a drive and the urge to vomit passed.

Trevor turned up again with Hannah as backing for John. Hannah said there was a sense that I was getting ready for the King. The King is enthralled with my beauty, I am the daughter of the most high God. Part of the royal priesthood, I must keep my head lifted high. I must accept that I am a princess.

The Lord has placed a robe of Righteousness on me, I am made in the image of God, reflecting His beauty.

Trevor told me to take every thought captive to Christ. If Jesus can calm the wind and waves, Jesus will calm the raging storm within, speak to the storm and it will calm down.

After the prayer session I made some silly excuse about wanting to spend some time on my own. John had a friend round so I went upstairs. Big mistake. Took food up with me. The TV was plastered with food as a programme about eating disorders was on. I couldn't turn it off. I was gripped with the images on the box. I binged and then vomited. I felt awful for being sick but when John's friend went we shared and I told him everything. I felt very dirty and had a long soak in the bath.

After confessing this to John, the Spirit manifested itself in bed again and it went on for a long time but John calmed it down. This was scary - it had never done this before while we were alone. I can't look at this as back to square one, I must pick myself up and start tomorrow where I left off. I was left with a ripping feeling in my throat and it feels very raw.

30th January 1998
I woke up feeling good, repented and guilt free. I changed my pattern

of eating slightly but at 3.00 pm felt panicky and the cravings were awful. John and I were both very tired from the fighting with the enemy the previous night. John was drained and was snappy with the children and we argued. I wanted to run out, get away from it all, but I must face situations like this and not take it personally because this does not mean that John hates me, it just means that he is weary. A breakthrough - I didn't turn to food. I had to force my dinner down and then live with the consequences of my stomach being bloated. It was uncomfortable.

The prayer time came and we shared with Charlotte and Jackie the turmoil of last night and the terrible day we had experienced. They agreed that John and I needed to be united because the enemy was glorifying in our fighting. John prayed into love, and said the spirits hated love, so he prayed a protection over the whole family and over the circle of people who were praying for me, then we hugged and re-affirmed our love for one another.

Charlotte read the story of the Prodigal Son - when the son was in a mess he went back to the father. The father opened his arms wide and ran to greet his son. No matter what, the Father will love us unconditionally.
(Isaiah 52) (Ephesians 1:4)(Luke 15:11-32)

31st January 1998
Today was a trying day. I had to force myself to eat again, then when I did eat had to beat the urge to carry on eating and not to binge. I succeeded, but it was difficult.

John and I had the same words from the Bible (Psalm 139) and it seemed so right for this period, as if this psalm was talking to the both of us.

Chapter 7

A very dear couple came round, Julia and her husband Kevin, and they prayed for us. They hadn't been all week so we recapped over the week's events. They are a very wise pair and said that we can do all things through Christ because he is strong for us and that we both have the Holy Spirit living within us and He is in control and won't allow us to go through more than we can cope with.

Julia said that Satan had attempted to separate us, but when we embraced we became one, and they prayed over us, seeing us both under a protective covering. She drew an image of a dome with John and myself inside. They told me not to be fearful of failure. Julia said the fear of failure will be dealt with. The spirits didn't manifest themselves tonight, though I felt I could keep them under control myself. The session was quiet and based on grace and love, and again we declared our love for each other before God.

It was true that I was fearful of letting everyone down. The following week did scare me but I have to trust in the Lord.

1st February 1998
Today I felt a real sense of freedom because I had no cravings to work through and it felt wonderful to have a total glimpse of independence. The world looks so different - it is like wearing glasses for the first time and seeing things clearly, God is so good, the trees look so beautiful, the birds sound lovely, the whole world is a miracle of creation and who can deny that God can work miracles if he can do all this? I feel that I have changed in my physical appearance. My hair, skin, nails and teeth feel different - my body is at last getting the nutrients it has yearned for.

I shared the above with Charlotte, Julia, Jackie and Diane. Jackie saw

me as a conduit for people in need and being a contact person who
will refer them on to appropriate helpers. Another had the same sort of
picture of many people coming to me with their problems, but I must
rest in the Lord.

We stood in a circle and sang worship to the Lord. I re-declared my
commitment to Jesus and confirmed that he is welcome to every part of
me! The parts I have held back over the years, I had to hand it to Him
at the Cross. I stood in the middle of the circle, the prayers were hands-
on and went clockwise. We had a wonderful time. John put his hand
near to my throat which stirred the spirit up. I pushed John's hand away
and I asked God not to let it rear its ugly head. It didn't.

2nd February 1998
The past week has seemed like a roller-coaster ride, sometimes so high
that I felt I was in the clouds, but then soaring down at a tremendous
speed to the pits of the earth. John has been with me 24 hours a day,
apart from the hour when I lapsed, which confirmed to John that I
shouldn't be left alone.

I woke up really refreshed, feeling a newness in my life. The cravings
returned but I tried to maintain a stable eating pattern, making sure I ate
in moderation and kept it down. I was training myself for a marathon.

Trevor and his wife Rebecca came round tonight. Trevor saw me as
Gideon - a mighty warrior. I felt ready to tackle some of the demons.
We began deliverance and it was a gentle time, breathing the spirits
out, from fears or cravings, fear of "blowing up", fear of fatness, fear
of love, fear of burdening others, fear of upsetting people, and spirit of
death. Prayed into cutting from the blood line with great grandmother.
Rebecca prophetically put my fears into a bag, pulled the drawstring

then she threw it into the sea and a sign of "no fishing!" placed over the area. The bag is never to be seen again.

3rd February 1998

I was at home alone today, so I decided to do a spot of decorating, thinking that I would be safe. The cravings were unbearable. I ate a biscuit then couldn't stop - it led to a full blown binge. Afterwards I felt awful, dirty, but it also felt different from the normal binge times. Again I picked myself up. I felt I wanted to fight more - repented and felt peace, the song "The battle is the Lord's" rang round in my head. I will defeat this problem, Jesus is so gentle.

Trevor and his son Brian came tonight for prayers. Trevor felt that I needed to unlock some layers with a key (layers of the onion). Spirit of father cut from my blood line, then the spirit was cut from me to my boys. Brian felt that I should deal with the father issue before going any further. John had a picture of me as David battling against Goliath, although I have to deal with many Goliaths and deal with their size, God's spirit inside me is bigger and stronger and I have enough pebbles to knock every (layer) Goliath down.

I shared some childhood experiences about my father which were prayed into and then I was delivered from them.

4th February 1998

It was John's birthday today and we went out for a meal to a lovely restaurant - nice company, disappointed with the food, especially as I wanted to eat it. I felt quite low and wanted to binge. John is showing signs of weakness, he is finding this month to be a testing time. John confessed to being unsettled, he was very tired and this resulted in his becoming sharp with me. My defences went back up.

The prayer hour came but I didn't want it. I wasn't feeling at all receptive. Trevor and Rebecca sensed this and suggested that John and Trevor go into the kitchen and they discussed John's feelings about my bingeing. John said he felt anger at the devil for attacking me whilst he wasn't around and anger towards himself for letting me talk him into leaving me. Trevor advised John to be aware of the spirit of deception and to realise that it wasn't me that was being cunning, it was the spirits within me.

I stayed in the lounge and spoke with Rebecca. She shared a picture that Lucy had given her of a little girl in a pretty white floral dress in a very large attic. The little girl was very angry and having a two year olds' temper tantrum. She was stomping her feet 'Bang, Bang, Bang!' but no-one noticed, no-one came. She then saw the little girl go into a corner of this attic room, stick her fingers in her ears and scream and scream and scream.

There was a skylight in this attic but the little girl was too little to see out. The attic was bare. We prophetically unlocked the attic door and walked out into freedom. I couldn't believe it - I hadn't shared my experiences in the attic with anyone. Obviously the little girl was me. It was a clear description of the large attic in Germany.

Trevor and John returned to the room and Trevor encouraged me to step out of the attic room, then he asked me to look into the large mirror in my lounge. It was torture and extremely difficult for me to do, and as I looked at myself, picking out all my negative points, I felt very uncomfortable and was tempted to keep looking away, repulsed at the reflection I was concentrating on. My throat tightened up again, but no spirits manifested.

I felt exhausted, very low and tearful. I could hardly speak and wanted to give up on everything, it is getting too much for me to handle. I prayed out to the Lord whilst in bed and said to the Lord, "I am weak, I need more strength to carry on..."

5th February 1998

I felt a bit better this morning. Lucy called with a picture she had had whilst praying at home for me. It was a picture of a little girl inside a fence, there was a gate, the girl went to the gate but it was locked, she looked down at the lock and cried "Let me out, Let me out!" But then she was locked out. I believe this related to the time when we lived in Leeds - under the blankets. It's amazing how God reveals things through prayer.

John felt that the devil was playing tricks at different times now, and he told me again and again how much he loved me. He put his arms around me and said "These are God's arms around you", and told me I was safe in the Lord's arms. John feels that I should get angry and tell the spirits to flee, and that I should declare to the spirits that I belong to the Lord, but I didn't want to listen, so John called around some of the intercessor team for prayer.

That evening, Diane, Christine and Trevor came for support in prayer. Diane likened me to (Joshua 18:3) to encourage me to continue and even though I am tired of fighting to continue - I must take possession of the land that God has given me.

John saw that I had a little girl spirit inside of me, he saw that my little girl years were stolen from me, also in this was a connected spirit of loneliness and John and I looked into each others eyes as the little girl spirit was leaving.

I prophetically walked out of the fenced area with Diane and Christine and we prayed for the breaking of relationship with Bulimia and to replace this friendship with a friendship with myself. Diane felt that I may go through a bereavement process and I felt I had already experienced this on the 28th January, but it hadn't seemed significant at the time. A name was given which didn't mean anything at the time - it sounded really stupid actually. To name this name would reveal the people who abused me as a child.

I was ready to battle on now that my strength was lifted.
(1 Corinthians 13:1-13)

6th February 1998
I had many attacks today - many binge cravings. I fought off many of the attacks, but John made me feel uneasy, calling me every five minutes. This made me feel un-trusted, so I had to get a small binge in. Trevor recognised a pattern forming: it seemed to be every fourth day that the binge relieved the stress and stopped the urges. I cooked the children's dinner and felt fine. The mistake I made was in not confessing this binge.

Even in the prayer hour when Charlotte and Brian attended, I was worried about what John would say. John prayed for a release of authority of men over me. Charlotte prayed for Paul and a release of any ties and for guidance in this area. Brian said "I'm sorry, Ella, I'm sorry for all the physical and emotional abuse, I stand as a representative of all men". He suggested that I find friendships with males and trust them (especially father figures) like Trevor or Kevin. I do find that I struggle with authority as I am quite a stubborn person and hate people telling me what to do.

Chapter 7

I feel the Lord is teaching me not to get stirred up when I am ordered/ instructed to do something. Over the last few days I had been told to do many things and had obeyed reluctantly, so I prayed for this spirit to be released.

I prayed for me not to doubt John's love and to accept it and trust him. Charlotte gave me a picture of a banana slowly being peeled back and the actual banana in the skin will be revealed, but be careful where the skin is thrown so that it is not there for someone else to slip on.

7th February 1998

I felt as though I wanted to carry on the brief binge I had earlier and I began planning for tomorrow. Bingeing spoke to John and released this and I felt guilty for not confessing to John about this earlier. I must do this. I couldn't sleep and in the middle of the night I woke him up and told him that I had binged. This stopped the planning ahead for tomorrow. We went back to sleep.

I woke again at 3 am overwhelmed by the attic images playing around in my mind - horrific memories. I have never shared the full story with anyone, it was too painful. I had been shocked at the picture given earlier on in the prayer month by Lucy. John awoke and the spirits started manifesting. I wept furiously and John was very supportive and loving. He prompted me to re-enter the attic and describe what had happened. As I spilled out this painful experience, the Lord revealed the Irish leprechaun to me - it was the black slimy smiling monster in my stomach.

I then told John of the names of the two people who had sexually abused me as a child, and their names amalgamated referred to the stupid name mentioned a couple of days ago. As John and I prayed for this spirit to leave, a ripping feeling was coming from my abdomen and there was an awful noise which thundered around the silence of the night. John and I were scared.

John ordered the spirit to leave in the name of Jesus and bundled it into the bag and threw it into the deep river. John then prayed for the waves to soak us. I also saw the waves - they were fierce, but when the bag hit the water it calmed and all that was left were the ripples where the baggage had dropped into the water, and it drowned the laughing leprechaun forever.

John saw for the first time the picture of the leprechaun. I had a dull ache in my chest. John felt the spirit trying to get into him and I was feeling peace. I looked into my inner self just to check that it wasn't hiding. I looked inside my legs, my arms - wow, what a relief!

It had been a long night and it was 5.30 am before we eventually got to sleep. John said I should have a bath, but I was too exhausted. I did have a bath when eventually I did awaken.

I was in a daze for most of the day. Both John and I were very emotional and wept together. Looking forward to the prayer hour, we started with the Lord's prayer and John shared of the early hours of the morning. He felt it was a real breakthrough. John had felt sick when the spirit had tried to enter him and he explained how he took command in Jesus' name. John said how he felt angry with the devil.

Doug was here tonight and we prayed for a release in sincerity, to look at the good and the bad points. John felt we had dealt with another layer and whilst we were praying Doug said he could see a deeper peace within me. We prayed to replace the empty space with more

Chapter 7

love, more kindness, more patience, and more confidence - overall, more like Jesus. The old baggage is being left behind but needs to be replaced by new.

I felt the Holy Spirit on me so strong. I saw a picture of a ray of sunshine pouring over the three of us from heaven and at the bottom of these beautiful beams of light were delicate sunflowers with the petals reaching up to the light. The heads weren't drooping any longer.

8th February 1998

John went to church today, but I couldn't face it - too many people. Mum and Dad came down for the day and we went to the seaside. It was nice, but I was under attack all day, it was a real battle. I had many cravings to work through. It was wonderful seeing my parents, but I don't think my mum fully understands what I am experiencing. We had a roast dinner, which was lovely, but also difficult.

John had a couple of words given to him at church where he was tearful and drained. He was told that the Lord would not put us through anything we couldn't handle, and that we were well equipped for what God wants to put there for us because He knows our limits.

In the prayer hour, Charlotte came in with the word "Happiness!" and I believe God gifted me with this tonight. Diane and Trevor prayed to lift John and me up again with loads of encouragement.

Rebecca didn't come this evening but gave these words to Trevor to give to me to read through - the notes on the Blood of Jesus:

1. I am cleansed from all sin by the blood of Jesus (1 John 1:7)
2. I am brought near to God by the blood of Christ (Eph 2:13)

3. I am justified by the blood of Jesus (Romans 5:8-9)
4. I have redemption through the blood of Jesus (Eph 1:7)
5. I am sanctified through the blood of Jesus (Heb 12:12)
6. I have peace with God through His blood (Col 1:20)
7. I am in a covenant relationship with God through the blood of Jesus (Mark 14:24)
8. I am purchased by the blood of Jesus (Acts 20:28)
9. The blood of Christ cleanses my conscience (Heb 9:14)
10. I have confidence to come into the presence of God by the blood of Jesus (Heb 10:19-22)
11. The blood of Christ is precious to me (1 Peter 1:19)

Focus on the above and realise what the Lord has done for us. John said it was not my will, or John's will for me to be healed, it was God's will for me to be fully cured so that he can use me for his good! Wow, what a calling!

We are halfway into the prayer month and it has been tough. It feels like we have been going for months, not days! Many more faces, more pictures, more prophecies. I feel unworthy to have all these words just for me. How will I ever fulfil them? If the Lord has these things in store for me, then I put my trust in Him and look forward to the day He wants to reveal them. A lot of doors had been opened with the keys the Lord has provided. John still feels the spirits that are left need to have anger shown to them.

CHAPTER EIGHT

Freedom

The past couple of weeks have been exhausting, both physically and mentally, with so many tears, but knowing Jesus brings such joy and fulfilment. Living with my eating disorder before I gave my life to Christ, I had no hope of healing, but now I see the light at the end of the tunnel and know the Lord has this victory.

I could not believe that you could cram so many spirits and feelings into one body and I didn't realise what was still waiting to be released. I know that I could not have come this far without the Lord and John, but I also believe that I had to come to this stage in my recovery process. I needed the secular counselling and I wanted to get to the point in my life when I would be ready to surrender the Bulimia.

My eating at this point was superb, I was eating regularly and I hadn't weighed myself once, but knew that I was gaining weight because my clothes were tightening around my waist, but this didn't worry me.

9th February 1998

I felt confident and happy today. I didn't make any sandwiches for myself in the morning. Came home for lunch, sat down to eat with John, briefly thought about being sick because felt uncomfortably full, resisted. Felt extremely bloated today, eaten a lot, still struggling with the craving thoughts, can't differentiate between hunger and cravings.

In the hour of prayer, we talked about this problem about hunger and cravings and Kevin and Julia prayed into this, prayed out the fear of food, fear of starvation and poverty. Felt very hot tonight when being prayed for, on all the other nights my whole body turned icy cold, but tonight my blood was boiling.

John prayed into the blood line again, prayed forgiveness for my mother, and in doing this Julia saw a picture from the Lord of a trauma during my mum's pregnancy.

She also saw a widow with black lace over her head - she was very old, grandmother maybe, she said. I remember my mum telling me a story of when she was pregnant with me when she walked into the room where my great-grandmother was holding a seance. My great-grandmother was angry at this and the spirits may have entered the womb even at this stage.

In the Lord's prayer there is a line with which I am sure everyone is familiar, "Give us this day our Daily Bread". Our 'Daily Bread' should be something to be enjoyed - even Jesus enjoyed socialising around food, so we prayed for a normality in eating habits, not too much, not too little, just the correct amount in daily intakes, trust in the Lord. Denying the daily bread is denying Jesus, after all, He is the bread of life. When everyone left I felt very strong and uplifted, aware that it is the fourth day tomorrow, we prayed a protection over this to try to break this pattern.
(Luke 11:3) (Luke7:9) (John 6:25-59)

10th February 1998
Today I started off badly and cravings hit me as soon as John walked out of the door this morning. He had to leave for an appointment in Norfolk and the devil waits to pounce on my weakness. I couldn't fight the temptation and binged before work. I called John and told him, and this gave me the bug to binge again in the afternoon, but I resisted.

Chapter 8

John felt today that I needed other people to speak to when I need to. I told him I found this very difficult to do because I feel so tearful and would probably not be able to talk, just cry! I didn't want to burden others or feel stupid and I was also scared of being rejected although I know deep down that people wouldn't do it purposely, it's just my insecurity. John said people were just waiting for me to pick up the phone and cry for help, and that people find it a pleasure to be involved in this and want to help.

In the evening, Doug came round. He had a real empathy with me and agreed with John that I need to open up to more people because I cannot rely on John all the time. He asked if I had a nickname as a child and I told him that 'Ella' is my nickname - my full name is Ellouise. He prayed "Ella, Ella, you are not a burden to your family, Ella you are not a burden to your church, Ella you are not a burden to God - he loves to take your burdens, the Lord delights in your burdens. Your burdens are lifted Ella, Ella, Ella". Each time he said my name he clicked his fingers.

They both prayed into the fear of rejection, accepting that friends are finding it a pleasure to help. John referred to me and could see people saying "I knew that lady, I helped her in that time of difficulty...". I personally don't feel worthy to think this, but I have had visions of me standing before an audience with my testimony (this terrifies the life out of me). I shake even standing at the front at a church meeting.

I shared about the two cartoon figures in my head who had been there as far back as I can remember. One is a little red devil, and of course the other is a sweet pure angel (what else?). As John prayed these figures away, there was a pain in my left ear, my neck gave way, the Holy Spirit covered me, I was burning up!

 # Living Behind the Mask

There had been a picture of a little girl with hands over her mouth and John thought that this was the time to share this picture as some root problems connected - Rejection - Rejecting herself. Again, this was me. I was told to equip myself daily with the Armour of God. I copied this out and placed it on my notice-board at work.

Death and Destruction trying to raise its head. John bound it back until the right time because I needed to use my will to resist and fight the enemy. John declared my sins are forgiven. I am pure as snow. (Ephesians 6)

11th February 1998
I felt under attack most of the day, not really feeling hungry but forcing myself to eat, but when I did eat I wanted to continue. John went out of the office and the desire to binge was overwhelming. I couldn't control it and recapped on what was discussed last night. I got to an hour of desperation - I was alone and called everyone I thought would be in - only answer-machines or "ring, ring, ring"! I had to call John and he prayed for me whilst in the car (this was the first time he has ever prayed over the phone). It worked. The cravings passed, and then I had phone call after phone call and one of the intercessors popped in the office for coffee. This was a real lifesaver. God is Good, the cravings passed.

In the evening we praised God for this victory, praying against the controlling personality and a renewing of the mind. They prayed for me to find out who I am and what my personality is.

Three very wise mature Christians came tonight and suggested that yesterday when my neck gave way could have been a trick from the enemy. The angel was the spirit on the left, the devil is so deceptive.

Chapter 8

I was asked to keep my eyes open and look into the eyes of one of the ladies, she shouted the spirit to leave and she could see it leaving through my eyes. My throat tightened up during the prayers but after I could feel a joy and peace.

A picture had been given a few days ago and it was time for me to see it. It was of a circus where the people don't speak English. There was a little girl in the ring, standing to one side, watching six clowns in full costume. The clowns start laughing, tormenting and mocking her and she closes her eyes, scrunches them up tight and puts her fingers in her ears.

The lady saw six clowns' faces close up, each one representing someone in my lifetime, clowns = masks.

1. Tormenting and mocking   -   Father
2. Blackness/Darkness from the past   -   Great-grandmother
3. Death/destruction/pain   -   Brother
4. More pain   -   Ex-husband
5. Loving and caring   -   John
6. Light (candle - happy)   -   God

Clowns are holding things...

1. 2 dolls and a teddy bear
2. 2 rings and 2 sets earrings
3. Bike
4. Coat and shoes
5. Plain gold ring and white dress
6. Crown - precious jewels

The lady didn't have a clue what the above meant. She hadn't been to the prayer evenings but had a vision of these whilst in the bath - she could see the faces coming towards me. I couldn't move, I was glued to the ground. I know who they all are, but I refuse to look behind the masks.

I had always hated clowns because of seeing the laughing clown at the seaside when I was younger. The eyes always looked evil and I assumed that they were real and that if they broke out of the glass case they would probably be murderers and come and find me when I sleep and kill me, then laugh in an evil roar. As you are probably aware, this fear gave me the inspiration for this book.

The people here this evening believed that I had a fear of humiliation and they prayed this out. I was exhausted.

12th February 1998
I didn't feel very well today. I had a sore throat and had to force myself to eat, but even managed to make the meal myself - a real breakthrough. I didn't have any cravings today. In the evening, prayed for fear and emotions to be re-installed, asked the Lord to let go of emotions.

John has said on a few occasions that he would like me to be released of my eating disorder and for him to have it, breaking all ties from the enemy in this. I wouldn't wish it on anyone but, without John knowing it, he was inviting trouble. We praised God for bringing us this far and for giving us the faith to carry on to press on to the Goal (30 days). Spoke about keeping the focus on God, not glorifying the devil.

John prayed for a release of fear from my Dad. Another picture had been given which read - Little girl again, heard footsteps coming down.

She was scared but showed no emotion. She hid under staircase. A man's voice was calling her name. She didn't see his face. She didn't make any noise. The fear was intense, but still she showed no emotion. Man went back upstairs and closed the door behind him.

The little girl didn't want to be found. She was holding all her emotions in. She didn't show anger or fear.

She knows the man's voice. She knew who it was. John asked if this rang any bells with me and I told a story of when my Dad was cooking on the barbecue at the bottom of the cellar stairs when he got angry at me and hit me with the hot rod of the barbecue forks. It wasn't so much the hitting of me with them, it was the hurt I felt at his doing it and I ran and ran and ended up running back into the house through the front door, down into the cellar, and hid under the stairs where I could hear my father calling me. I was so fearful that I couldn't speak and I wanted him to suffer, to feel pain, and, hopefully, to worry about me. When I eventually surfaced, he did apologise.

13th February 1998

I wanted to resist eating but I knew that I must keep topped up by eating regularly. Feel like carrying on eating after a meal and spoke to John about it, it is really difficult. I still don't feel right, not the least bit hungry but know I must eat. I felt bloated after eating and was very uncomfortable. I was still feeling unwell, and claustrophobic with so many people coming around the house. John was there constantly and I did want to get better and I was feeling better, being able to eat and keep it down is a big step forward, having days without bingeing is a fight but I have a real sense of satisfaction.

John didn't have any pointers, no pictures, no feelings about the day for the prayers. Three women came tonight and it's funny because John thought this week would be male-dominated. John asked if anyone else had any ideas and it was suggested that I confess anything that was unconfessed, but I couldn't think of anything. John said that because I was under the weather it would be best to take the focus away from me, so they asked the Lord for a strengthening in John.

We gave thanks to God, and prayed generally, asking the Lord for a birth of new Christians through our network of friends. I said there was a strong connection between eating disorders, alcoholism, and drug abuse.

John said we were entering a new phase and that, although the root had been removed the other night, there were still some layers to remove. When everyone had gone, I had a look through my self-help manual and shocked myself at how far I really had come in such a short space of time, then John and I went through my old monitor sheets. It was the first time that I had shown them to John and he couldn't believe it, and just said, "Where was I? All that food eaten. What was I doing?". He was shocked, but proud that I had broken through the major barriers.

14th February 1998
Valentine's Day! I was in love with Jesus and I wanted to shout it from the roof tops. Jesus is alive! It was the fourth day again but I feel very strong. As a family, we kept busy all day and John even left me a couple of times, with no lapses.

The prayer time came around quickly. John said we should pray for my brother, especially for how badly I had treated him in our childhood. I shared some experiences and prayed forgiveness over our parents to release them, they thought I was an independent child and didn't need affection. One man who had been particularly devoted to this prayer month, and who had attended most evenings, changed the way I thought about older men. I looked upon him as a father figure and I could say anything to him. He prayed for the spirit of control to go. The spirit manifested itself and they saw a spirit of incest in the family and asked for it to be broken from me, particularly ties that could have skipped from me into my children.

I had my usual bath and looked down at my now curvy body. I wasn't feeling comfortable with these new curves (not fat) and I shared this with John but he misunderstood what I was saying. I was being honest about my feelings, not really wanting any advice and as John had told me to be open, I was obeying. John's reaction, however, was 'No diets!' but this wasn't what I was getting at and when he suggested that I exercise, immediately alarm bells started ringing. I felt I must be looking out of shape, unattractive, just when I thought I was feeling comfortable.

John asked me to look into his eyes, but I didn't want to, I just wanted to run, run away as far as possible. He asked me who the Lord of my life was. I shut my eyes tight and when I shut them I saw myself with teeth growing long and sharp, red eyes, long sharp nails like razors ready to gouge at John's face (like a werewolf). The light was blinding, I wanted John to turn it off.

John continued to pray and commanded the spirit to settle down or reveal itself. I was very tired by now! John felt we needed to pray for the clown's faces again, especially the one of John, so we prayed in love, a strength of the marriage covenant, wives to submit to husband as to the Lord.
The devil wanted a last attempt on the fourth day to get me to

binge. John said the person earlier was not me and that I was being attacked. John said he couldn't let me run or hide and he followed me everywhere. He said there was hatred in my eyes and he told me to keep my eyes open. The spirit wouldn't name itself but John bound it back, then prayed for deliverance for me over his control, his leadership, his domination. I quietened down, I was back. Thank you Lord. John felt the Lord say we two are one.
(Genesis 2:18-24) (Ephesians 5:21-33)

15th February 1998
Well, we were doing great up until 3 pm when we sat down to dinner as a family and John and I ended up arguing. I felt a real hatred for John, he made me feel rejected. I had to get away from him, went out for a drive, went to the office and prayed. Later I phoned John to see if it was okay for me to return - I thought he hated me and would never want me back again, and that this was the end of our relationship. Of course he welcomed me back. I apologised and John said he could see it wasn't me, that hatred was back in my eyes. On the positive side - I didn't binge.

In the prayer hour, when John shared what had happened last night and today, he broke down in tears and said that he had failed me. He had pushed me away when he should have prayed for me. We prayed for strength and encouragement for John. We agreed there were no winners in arguments, we are just going through the differences between Men and Women.

John had a picture of five banners being held over the two of us, they were coloured red, blue, green and yellow, but he couldn't identify the last one. One of the women had brought her banners in the bag and the last colour was white, which represented being pure. I saw this flag as the surrender flag, I had to surrender my eating disorder to God. When everyone left, John read Song of Songs 7 to me, and it was very touching.

(2 Corinthians 4:7-18)

16th February 1998

It was the sixth day today without bingeing - incredible! However, home alone today, it was destined to happen - binged, I was rewarding myself for doing so well, but felt awful afterwards. What a horrid compensation, it was more like a punishment. On the positive side, the binge wasn't as bad as it had been previously.

In the evening I was feeling quite low and I prayed for the Bulimia to flee. John saw a picture of twins, Bulimia and Anorexia, and said that he felt that it was time to give up old friends and welcome two new ones, Jesus and the Holy Spirit. There was a real battle going on, the ripping feeling from my throat left me feeling like I had a mouthful of blood. It was disgusting. They could see a serpent around my throat.

To end of the evening we prayed about love and grace and they all attempted to build me up after my ordeal. John was worried because we only had seven days left. Trevor discussed what God had created in just seven days, and John read Genesis - The Creation. Glorified God for the fourth day pattern being broken and extended to the sixth.

17th February 1998

A friend called up first thing in the morning and gave me some words to meditate on for the day - "Hunger and Thirst after Righteousness". I had today off work again because one of the children was ill. I must be strong. Friends phoned or came round just at the right time and John came home early and worked from home. I was snappy with him but we talked and I became tearful.

John suggested that I go upstairs and pray. I went into the bedroom alone and asked the Lord to reveal to me why I was feeling like this, especially because we had prayed for the twins Bulimia and Anorexia to leave. God spoke to me through the word in James and I realised that I had a dis-order with myself.

I didn't feel like I wanted to binge but, as John quite rightly said, he was there (my safety net!). Yesterday dealt with the twins, today needed to pray in triplets, the Trinity - Father-Son-Holy Spirit. Needed to pray out the dark side Hatred-Jealousy-Selfishness, which is the result of Bulimia/Anorexia which is such a selfish problem.

I wasn't looking forward to 6.30 pm. Two dear sisters close to my heart arrived and we prayed that the circle of trust would not be broken, all that is said must be confined to the circle of people involved in prayers, and this will allow me to hold on to my dignity and enable me to proceed to minister help to other people. A picture of a rose, beautiful but thorny, but Jesus is the gardener and he is breaking off all the thorns, so that there are no thorns to block or injure me - inside or out. The soothing healing oil from the Spirit of God will wash over any wounds and heal them, there will be no thorns anywhere, especially blocking the throat, leaving the beauty of the pure rose as the person of Jesus "Trust in the Lord for all things".

It was suggested that I had a Jezebel spirit which needed to be dealt with, and they also thought I needed a protection and a cleansing of my womb. We didn't have time to do this but John wrote it down as a to-do prayer. (Psalm 143-144) (James 3:3-18) (Ephesians 5:21-33)
18th February 1998

Chapter 8

Today has been very busy, but there have been no attacks from the enemy. John didn't really have a specific focus for the evening and I, too, didn't have anything strong, so in the evening I prayed a protection over the house, over the children - a healing over the boys.

The children have been very patient over this past month. They have had people wandering in and out, and they have been confined to the spare room. They have all been extremely good, thank the Lord!

John declared that they are 'our' children, not 'mine' and 'yours', maybe not through the blood line but in love. I cannot fully absorb this statement because John has said on frequent occasions "I can never love the boys the same as the girls". There has always been this division and this, to me, is a warning "Hold back they are mine!".

John prayed over Joshua's insecurities, especially any vibrations he may have inherited from me.

It was suggested that I set up some sort of self-help group and I already had this in mind for the future, but realise that I have to concentrate on my own healing first.

A picture of me in a wedding dress with a veil that trailed down to the floor - prayed for a lifting of the veil. Even when I am suffering by the toilet, throwing up, with a tear-stained face, God will lift the veil and say "Arise my love, my fair one ..." (Song of Songs). This has relevance to all areas of my life, when I am feeling unable to face God, because of how ashamed I am feeling about what I am doing. The Lord lifts the veil and my face shines for Him.

After the session, I felt dirty, not cleansed and this feeling increased later. I had a sense of freedom from the prayers, another night off from the 30 days, the focus was going off me. I had an unhealthy cunning feeling and started to plan for a binge tomorrow when John was due to be away for most of the day. I felt scared/taken-over and very rebellious, with "I don't care" feelings. Scared after coming so far. John says I have to be strong, I made an appointment to see a friend tomorrow, overwhelming desire to cancel, stay at home and binge!

I can't get rid of these thoughts. As the evening wore on I felt depressed and when John prayed for me I had a blockage in my throat which felt like having a tablet trapped in my windpipe, but eventually it eased and then disappeared.

19th February 1998

I had two hot meals today, and felt good about it. John and I had a misunderstanding again today and we need to communicate and have empathy with each other. The boys are still ill and this is very draining in itself. If nothing else, John and I have learned to pray together this month.

Three people came for the prayers tonight and with so many demons having been dealt with, to make me feel like I'm not totally infested with evil spirits, we focused on the Lord and we looked at the miracles that God has performed so far. Tonight they said that I had a maturity about me, a strong daughter alive for the Lord.

One of the ladies felt pins and needles down her arms into her hands and she said she needed to use this power for healing, so she prayed over my throat, my stomach, oesophagus, hands and ankles. John said for me to place walking boots on to walk the nations, spreading the word of God's healing, and they requested the gift of healing be given to me.

John said for me to get on a bike and learn how to ride and never to forget, and although I may fall off a couple of times I should pick the bike up again and carry on. I saw this as my eating disorder. I have learned over this month how to eat normally, so must keep moving forwards. I have had a few setbacks, but the Lord has picked me up and pushed me along again. I asked the Lord to help me on my bike ride to continue moving forward and not to go back again. If I fall, look to the Lord and He will pick up the pieces and put them back together.

"Perfect love casts out fear", to break all fear of being left alone next month, in this vulnerable time. I must focus on the fact that I am never alone, Jesus is my best friend and he is there to help but also there are friends at hand to help and John is there for my strength.

20th February 1998

"If our God is for us then who can be against us?" (Romans 8:31)
I felt weak today, so phoned John to come home, the cravings were bad and I had to fight them. When John went out later to collect the girls, I found that the boys had left their sandwiches and I felt it was a waste, but I focused on God asked him to give me the strength to stop a full binge. I ate the sandwiches, then a packet of crisps, then prayed to God in desperation - I would have to live with the consequences of this. I looked in the mirror and prayed out the hatred in my eyes, prophetically lifted the veil and gave thanks and victory to the Lord.

I feel that when I binge I am being disobedient to God, who would not want me to purposely damage my body. When I next get the urge to binge I must concentrate on this. I feel I am going against my new freedom and my new identity. I have to put God into focus and remove the blurred vision when the urge to binge is overwhelming.

I felt tonight that I needed to deal with the strongman spirit. The history of the strongman was discussed, Death and Destruction, the Anti-Christ and Jezebel.

I felt Death and Destruction had been dealt with, and the Anti-Christ was sorted when I asked the Lord into my life. Tonight was the night for the Jezebel spirit!

I repented of the binge today and prayed King of Kings, Lord of Lords will have the victory. When the ground is hard and firm, it is hard to break it up with the fork, but once the ground has been dug over and the stones have been picked out, it is such a pleasure to hoe the ground and pick at the weeds - we are now at the weeding stage.

It was a heavy prayer session and John saw these last few days as a mountain, not the final hurdle, and I would be like a gazelle flying high over the mountain. There wasn't much deliverance and it was very calm.

I see binges like a huge vacuum where, usually, the binge sucks me in deep, but today the suction wasn't strong enough to do so. I was sucked in half way, then pulled out by the Lord's power when the vacuum continued to suck but then the power was switched off. I heard a screaming noise as the motor wound down.
(Romans 3:23) (Romans 5:8) (Matthew 22:37)

21st February 1998
This morning, I went to a meeting with the Full Gospel Businessmens' Fellowship for a prayer breakfast, when I surprised myself and ate

more than usual without feeling guilty. The guest speaker was Bill Isaacs-Sodeye, and he spoke on healing. His testimony was almighty. When he said he could see a young lady who had been through a big ordeal and she is being nudged by the Holy Spirit, I was convinced it was me! I couldn't stand. What if it wasn't me? So many times I had seen in prayer events that when someone stood, they were alone. I asked John to join me for moral support and, as I stood up from my seat, Bill pointed to me and said he had been waiting for me. There was a queue for healing prayer but he pushed this line of people aside and asked me to come forward.

He placed some ointment on my head and said "The Lord wants to use you to gossip about Him, He wants to use you to preach the gospel, using your experiences.

Please repeat after me - "I surrender my life fully to You, every part of my body from head to foot, my whole heart is Yours, You will use my hands, Lord take my life and use it for Your will, You have brought me through these trials for Your good, use them dear Lord".

As I repeated this, he could see various things, many of which I can't remember, but what remains prominent in my mind is that he said that I am now cleansed, the Lord has cleaned me throughout, I need to take up my Cross daily now and walk with Jesus each day, Jesus will use me through my words, the house is washed clean! Wow! It was impossible for this man to have known anything about me, he had come from Nigeria and didn't even know my name. I was floating for the rest of the day.

It was pouring with rain outside. We went to John's parents' house and I wanted to tell everyone what I had experienced, but now wasn't the right time. I had a wonderful afternoon.

In the evening there was an aura of peace around the house. Everyone felt this strong sense we prayed into the family, and wherever the children may live at different times, we will always be a whole and holy family of six. One person who came saw me in a long full white veil with sparkles - a symbol of purity (this person didn't know of the picture given on the 18th). She also saw me as the phoenix rising from the ashes, Venus from the sea, Gold purified in the crucible. These all represent me as reborn and able to go forward in strength and power - a beautiful transformation. Like the fairytale "Cinderella", I have been brought out from the ashes and made into a princess of the highest King, "Ella of the Cinders".

Pure Gold put in the fire comes out of it proven pure; genuine faith put through the suffering comes out proven genuine. When Jesus wraps this up, it's your faith, not your gold, that God will have on display as evidence of his victory.
(1 Peter 1:7)

22nd February 1998
Today was Sunday and I still didn't feel able to go to a church meeting, but ate normally, eating three regular meals with snacks.

This evening would be held at one of the church leaders' homes, not at our house, we had the Lord's victory!

We arrived at the later time of 8 pm to find the house was packed for a night of celebration and there was worship and banners. I was healed emotionally and we still had a day to go, I was cleansed and spiritually clothed with the Holy Spirit. The physical part was up to me.

John and I gave an account of the month's events and we shared the gradual steps the Lord had taken us through, and then had a time of prayer for various people's needs. I was told that I had a healing anointing authorised by God and was given a white flag to represent purity (cleansed through).

We ended the evening by holding up a green flag which everyone in the room walked under, representing Newness - walking from old to new. The Holy Spirit worked in a peaceful way.

We sang the song *"Do you believe in miracles, like I believe in miracles?"*.

CHAPTER NINE

Walking by faith

When we arrived home from the prayer evening, John physically collapsed. Lucy phoned and prayed for John over the phone as he lay in bed all cold and sweaty although to the touch he felt boiling. He was shaking and totally drained - the month had worn him out.

23rd February 1998

On the final day of prayer, John still hadn't moved from his bed and I was worried - I was walking the final day alone. I binged, scared of what was ahead, but the Lord was talking through the children. Daniel commented on how much I was eating, then after I had been vomiting, he said he could smell sick. I felt awful. I had been healed - the house is clean. It had been the last attempt from the enemy to buy back his ground, but I was determined to carry on.

I confessed my lapse to John and, in my own mind, agreed that I would confess immediately if it happened again, to eliminate the secrecy. In the prayer hour, Trevor, Brian and his two brothers arrived and if this had been earlier on in the month I don't think I could have handled it. The four surrounded me and prayed over me, prophetically. representing the four almighty angels around the Lord's throne: one had the face of a man, for mankind; one had the face of a calf, representing the workhorse; one had the face of the eagle soaring in the air; and the fourth had the face of the lion, the king of the beasts, and they were there to guard me. John lay asleep in bed.

Brian had a picture of me carrying my baggage over the hill, then throwing it over edge onto a heap of used luggage. Behind me is a long line of people carrying their baggage who will follow suit and chuck their bags over the hill. Mick had a picture of an egg and I am the chick breaking out of the egg, spreading my wings and moving on. The hen is Jesus and I should waddle behind the hen.

I have had many people approaching me with eating disorders and I didn't realise the extent of the problem - even within the church. We pushed the boat out for the final day and prayed a release for John, that he shouldn't be my strength any more - he is my covering.

24th February 1998

I surprised myself by how far I had come. I felt a freedom, free from any spirits attached to Bulimia, although the actual physical symptoms still needed to be dealt with. The mental side of Bulimia had been taken away by the Lord. I now had a choice, having dealt with the emotional and spiritual part of my illness, the physical symptoms will fade away, but will still need to be worked on.

The next week was a struggle, but I managed to eat normally. God was giving me a sense of normality, but the enemy was attacking. John stayed in bed all week and I was left to run the business, look after the house, cook the meals, and care for the children - Wow, was I in at the deep end!

This whole month has been a battle. I have had a few lapses, but felt dreadful after and experienced hot sweats and shaking. I realise that the time is coming for the physical strain of Bulimia to be lifted. John recovered and I still had covering from the prayer team. Our baptism is at 7.15pm on the 28th March, and it is no surprise that we are having attacks from the enemy - the last thing he wants is for us to be free.

I know the Lord wants to use my experiences and I have had enough prophecies to say this. I have many ideas, but I felt an urge to write of my experiences, I started writing my autobiography today, I didn't know at the time whether I would finish it, or if I did, that it would be in six months' time.

You can see on the table below how far my eating had advanced without condemning myself or jumping on and off the weighing scales.

Time	Drink and Food intake	Room	Vomit/Overeat feeling
7.45am	Cup of tea	Bedroom	I will be alone all day again
8.30am	Black coffee, bowl cereals, apple	Bedroom	
9.30am	Scone, black coffee	Office	
10.45am	Can coke	Office	
11.55am	Black coffee, sandwich, orange	Office	Wanted to get lunch out of the way, distracted by it being there
2.30pm	Black coffee, bag crisps	Office	Don't feel very well, bad headache
4.00pm	Cup of tea, scone	Kitchen	
5.30pm	Black coffee, risotto with vegetables	Kitchen	Had a long soak in the bath
7.30pm	Cup of tea, scone	Kitchen	
9.30pm	Cup of tea, biscuit	Bedroom	
10.15pm	Cup of tea, slice toast	Lounge	

Food Diary: 27th February 1998

Little did I know that the Lord had His hand on this book which He wanted to use sooner than later. I got onto the computer as and when I had time, and on the 29th March 1998, I completed my book. It is a miracle. The book might be published, but even if it isn't, I have gained an understanding of myself by writing everything down on paper.

I understand that not everyone may feel that they could go through such a month of turmoil, but, having read my life story, you will be aware that I had to take steps because an eating disorder cannot go overnight - it needs to be worked at. But God can heal and He will do it whilst retaining a person's dignity.

There are practical steps to work on but, to be cured fully, a person must be truthful to themselves, to a trustworthy close friend or relative, and, of course, confess to the Lord.

As you can see, my life wasn't easy and I had a lifetime of hurts and trials to work through. The painful experiences I had needed to be cared for and I had wounds that needed to be healed. With the help of the Lord I had to train my body to eat and digest food regularly. Many times I had to force myself to eat, and this last month wasn't easy and I often lapsed, but perhaps I needed to go through these difficult times to enable me to help others.

John and I had so many attacks from the enemy during this month and the business got to the stage where it almost folded. Our successful business was nearly destroyed by delaying payment of their bills and we were both very stressed. We weren't getting on and I felt isolated and that John wasn't understanding me.

I disguised the fact that I had binged and that I was not fully healed, and was scared to tell John. He shouted at me and told me to get angry with this thing. I wanted to back out from the baptism on the 28th because there were so many people saying they would be there to see it and I didn't want all this attention.

I spoke to Charlotte and Hannah who thought that maybe my problem was hormonal. My health wasn't too good so I went to my doctor who has put me on a course of tablets which should alleviate my symptoms. We are getting together to pray for this problem - irregular periods and hormonal problems can aggravate Bulimia, making pre-menstrual tension even worse for an eating disorder sufferer.

My doctor put me on tablets to regularise my periods to the day, and advised me to avoid coffee, sugar, and salty foods for ten days before my menstruation but to still maintain a healthy diet with plenty of fruit and vegetables. He also advised me to take gentle exercise. I was already taking vitamin B supplements but he suggested that I take evening primrose oil.

Over this past month I hadn't slept very well and would wake in the middle of the night feeling very tired, but I had some very special times with the Lord and He revealed so much to me in these lonely nights that I believe God disturbed my sleep so that He had my full attention. My concentration was on Him as I worked through the lingering physical symptoms of Bulimia.

I had many conflicting feelings about our baptism, even up to the final week. I wanted to cancel, but I knew that this was what the enemy wanted. The Lord desires me to give myself fully to Him and to say goodbye to the past, as He gave His life for me and rose again from the dead, He wants me to die to the old and rise out of the water a new being. My feelings changed, I felt nervous about tomorrow. My mother telephoned and said that she couldn't make it, so none of our family were going to be there, not blood family anyway. Our family in Christ would be there and we had a few non-believers coming, which was really touching and exciting! What impact would this have on them?

28th March 1998

We had a wonderful day as a family. John and I took the children to the cinema and we watched a film about fairies, a lovely film, and funny. Even as I sat in my seat I felt the Holy Spirit moving over my body and realised what today meant - the Lord was with me through everything and the angels were preparing for a celebration tonight when we gave our lives totally to God.

As usual, we had a very busy Saturday, with the children being very demanding and needing to be entertained throughout the day. They are very creative and made some lovely presents for us which made me realise why the little things a child gives to a parent makes them feel so proud, because to them it isn't something little, it is a gift which they have created and want to present to you, because they know you will get pleasure from it.

So it is with the Lord. He delights in the little things we do for Him, they make all the difference and He gives back in abundance.

Daniel said something funny. He knew that we were being baptised in the evening but hadn't listened properly to what was happening, so when we sat at the dinner table he asked me, "Mummy, what is crucified?". I told him it is when a person is nailed to a cross and dies a very sad death, like Jesus did. Horrified, he asked if we would come to life again? I was a little puzzled, but replied that Jesus had come to life again, but I hadn't heard of anyone else raised from the dead.

Daniel then asked why we were we going to the swimming pool? Then I realised what he meant - he thought baptism was crucifixion! He had mixed up the two words! But, on thinking about it, he wasn't so wrong. We are sacrificing our lives fully for the Lord when we are totally submerged in water because this is an act of killing the old and raising the new out of the water, cleansed. Bless him.

7 pm came round quickly and we packed our bags and drove to the local swimming baths where the church had hired the pool for an hour. Many familiar faces were around the pool and we had a time of prayer and worship. John and I gave a brief testimony and John said that as soon as he had given his life to the Lord he had longed to be baptised. I explained that I had felt the opposite, that I hadn't been ready for baptism until now because I suppose I hadn't been ready to give my life fully, but now I was cleansed and needed to be thoroughly soaked as a symbol of submitting my whole life to God.

The church leader gave us a brief outline of what baptism represents, and then we walked into the water. I went first and, as I plunged into the water, I said goodbye fully to Bulimia as it washed away through the pool filters, never to be seen again. I was totally healed! Halleluia! As I came out of the water, there was a huge cheer and we sang worship to the Lord. Jackie was waiting there with a towel, to greet me.

Next, it was John's turn and as I watched, taking in exactly what had happened to me, I felt a real sense of peace. The Holy Spirit surrounded the room and the lifeguards watched, but I don't think they could take in what was happening. It was a time of celebration.

John prayed that the Lord should use us for whatever He wants as we are servants to Him and are available for service. Our church leader said that through this act we had put a seal on our past lives and that the keys had been thrown away, we will not be affected by past hurts and experiences any longer, and are new births into the Kingdom of Christ.

Julia came up to me and hugged me, saying that the angels are rejoicing in Heaven, as this past month was a month of testing and we needed this time to dispose of any lingering remains of our untidy former life. We thanked everyone for being there and, as we said our goodbyes, we received a certificate of baptism and friends gave us some cards to congratulate us.

John and I held hands as we stood in puddles of water, united. It was so significant that John and myself had shared our walk with the Lord. My barrier shields have been removed and this is only the beginning.

Jesus is the Lord of my life and I am no longer ***Living behind the Mask!***

If there is anyone out there suffering with an eating disorder who feels there is no hope, know that there is a hope - Jesus. If you are willing to take the steps towards being free, I assure you it can be done, for no matter how bad or good you feel your problem is, Jesus can take it away from you. However, you must admit that you have a problem, then face it, share it with another, then go and see your doctor. If you don't feel you could cope with any of these, get in touch with an organisation who specialises in eating disorders and they could point you in the right direction.

Chapter 9

Go to church and meet Jesus. The thought of this probably terrifies you, and this is natural, but if you are determined to remove your mask, although it won't necessarily be easy, the Lord is gentle and ill not push you too fast. Trust in Him.

Living Behind the Mask

Living Behind the Mask